Key Stage 3 Science National Strategy Workbooks

These books have been written specifically to cover the Scheme of Work. That means they also cover the Yearly Teaching Objectives.

Each unit in the book covers one unit from the Scheme of Work. And there's even the odd ever-so-nearly entertaining bit, just to help keep you awake.

What CGP is all about

Our sole aim here at CGP is to produce the highest quality books — carefully written, immaculately presented and dangerously close to being funny.

Then we work our socks off to get them out to you — at the cheapest possible prices.

Contents

Unit 9A — Inheritance and Selection

Unit 9B — Fit and Healthy

Unit 9C — Plants and Photosynthesis

Unit 9D — Plants for Food

Unit 9E — Reactions of Metals and Metal Compounds

Unit 9F — Patterns of Reactivity

Contents

Unit 9G — Environmental Chemistry

Unit 9H — Using Chemistry

Unit 9I — Energy and Electricity

Unit 9J — Gravity and Space

Unit 9K — Speeding Up

Unit 9L — Pressure and Moments

Unit 9M — Investigating Scientific Questions

Published by Coordination Group Publications Ltd.

Contributors:
Jane Cartwright
Neil Fisher
Paddy Gannon
Gemma Hallam
Keith Hudson
Philippa Hulme
Steven Parkinson
Jim Wilson

Design and Graphics by:
Chris Dennett
Dominic Hall
Simon Little
Becky May
Joanne Morgan
Alison Palin
Katherine Reed
Julie Schofield
Claire Thompson
James Paul Wallis
Chrissy Williams

With Thanks to:
David Worthington and Eileen Worthington for the proofreading.

ISBN: 978 1 84146 244 8

Groovy website: www.cgpbooks.co.uk
Printed by Elanders Hindson Ltd, Newcastle upon Tyne.

Inherited Characteristics

Q1 Sarah is writing about herself in a letter to her new pen friend. She writes...

> I'm 160cm tall and I'm average build. I've long, light brown hair and my eyes are blue. I have freckles and pierced ears. I like sport and am good at running (I represented my school at county championships). My favourite subject is maths, I find it easy as Mum's a maths teacher and can help me. I like pop music and watching 'Eastenders'.

a) Write down three things about Sarah which are likely to be **inherited**.

b) Write down three things about Sarah which are likely to be **environmental** (not inherited).

c) Write down one thing which is likely to be decided by a mixture of inherited **and** environmental factors.

Q2 Andrew saves a conker from the tree at the end of his road and plants it in the garden. From the list below copy down the things you would expect to be the same for the new tree (when it has grown) and the old tree.

shape of the leaves, height of the tree, leaf colour, number of branches, flower colour

Q3 Write down whether each sentence about inherited characteristics is TRUE or FALSE.

a) Genetic information is in the nucleus of a cell.

b) A child gets all their genetic information from the egg cell nucleus.

c) Brothers and sisters have exactly the same genetic information.

d) Twins can be two girls, two boys or a girl and a boy.

e) Identical twins are formed from one egg fertilised by two sperms.

f) Fertilisation is when the nuclei of two sex cells combine.

g) In a plant, fertilisation happens when a pollen cell nucleus joins with a seed.

h) Sperm cells have tails as an adaptation to enable them to reach the egg.

Q4 Copy out the table and complete it using the words from the grey box.

Hint: You can use words more than once.

	Animal	Plant
Female sex cell		
Female sex cell produced in		____ in ____
Male sex cell		
Male sex cell produced in		
Fertilisation happens when	____ nucleus joins with ____ nucleus	____ nucleus joins with ____
Fertilisation produces		____ containing an ____

SEED
EGG (OVUM)
EMBRYO
POLLEN GRAIN
SPERM
OVARY
ANTHER
OVULE
TESTES

Variation

Q1 Sandeep and Helen have been having an exciting time measuring the masses of lots of potatoes. These are their results:

155g, 124g, 143g, 162g, 111g, 147g, 127g, 149g, 153g, 154g, 115g, 119g, 122g, 123g, 151g, 128g, 133g, 158g

a) Copy and complete this table.

Mass (g)	110-114	115-119	120-124	125-129	130-134	135-139	140-144	145-149	150-154	155-159	160-164
Frequency											

b) Draw a chart or graph of the results.

c) Their teacher asks them how many different **varieties** of potato they think they have in their sample. Write down how many you think there are and why.

d) How many potatoes of each variety had they been given?

e) How did the amount of variation in the varieties compare?

f) Copy and complete this sentence using the words "within" and "between".
For the potatoes, variation .... the varieties was greater than variation .... the varieties.

g) Suggest some factors other than mass which might be different between the varieties.

Q2 Write down TRUE or FALSE for each of these statements.

a) Cuttings taken from the same plant have identical genes.

b) The plants grown from the cuttings will also be identical.

c) Fraternal (non-identical) twins grow from two eggs separately fertilised.

d) Fraternal twins are genetically more alike than ordinary brothers and sisters but less alike than identical twins.

e) Environmental factors will result in differences even between identical twins.

Q3 A ewe gives birth to identical twin lambs but is not able to look after them both and one is hand-reared.

a) Write down things from the list below which could be different for the two lambs when they are older.

SIZE, COAT COLOUR, EYE COLOUR, MASS, BEHAVIOUR, HEALTH

b) Write down two factors which could cause there to be differences between the lambs.

c) What 'E' is the name for the sort of factor that causes differences between identical animals?

Selective Breeding — Animals

Q1 The table below lists the show **categories** at Cruft's dog show, one example **breed** of each category and a useful **characteristic** of that breed.

Category	Breed	Job	Characteristic
Gundog	Labrador		Good in water
Hound	Greyhound		Good sprint speed
Pastoral	Border collie		Intelligent and agile
Terrier	Scottish terrier		Good diggers
Toy	Pug		Small and quiet
Utility	Dalmatian		Able to run a long way
Working	Rottweiler		Aggressive

a) The list below gives the JOB each breed was supposed to do.
Copy the table and put these jobs in the correct box in the "job" column.

GUARD DOG, CARRIAGE DOG, CHASING HARES, HERDING SHEEP, COMPANION, RETRIEVING GAME, GETTING HUNTED ANIMALS OUT OF THEIR DENS

b) Robert is a Labrador breeder and his ambition is to breed a Cruft's champion. He decides he wants to produce a larger dog. He has several different male and female dogs to choose from for breeding and keeps some puppies from each litter to breed from later.

i) Describe what he should do to eventually get a larger dog.

ii) What 's' is the type of breeding he is attempting?

iii) There is one thing he should not do — what? and why not?

c) Copy and complete these sentences about selective breeding in terms of cells.

i) An inherited characteristic is controlled by ....

ii) Genes are contained in the genetic material in a cell's ....

iii) Sex cells contain .... the genetic material of a body cell.

iv) Sexual reproduction involves two .... cell nuclei joining together.

v) .... breeding relies on desirable characteristics being passed on in the .... contained in the sex cell's ....

I crossed a Bulldog with a shih-tzu once — I got a dogtzu...

Selective breeding is all about enhancing particular characteristics in animals and plants. If it's left to nature, the fittest survive, but when *we* start tampering we turn wolves into lap dogs — urrrgh!

Selective Breeding — Animals

Q1 Modern farm animals are quite different from those of 200 years ago due to selective breeding. Eg Hens lay more eggs each year. For each of the animals below write down one thing the breeders might have wanted to achieve.

a) Beef cattle

b) Dairy cattle

c) Sheep produced for meat

d) Sheep produced for wool

e) Pigs

Q2 The pictures below show three different types of cattle.

Hereford (European beef production)

Friesian (European milk production)

N'Dama (African meat, milk and field work)

Herefords produce more meat than N'Damas, and Friesians produce more milk than N'Damas. Write down two suggestions why Herefords or Friesians would not be any use in Africa.

Q3 Read this passage and then answer the questions below.

> Most West African countries have large populations of the N'Dama cattle. These cattle are resistant to a parasite which quickly kills other breeds and is common in that area. The cattle are relatively small but their milk and meat production levels are close to other African breeds which live in parasite-free areas or which need drugs to protect them. There is hope that selective breeding will further increase resistance as the N'Dama have a high level of genetic diversity.

a) Write down the most important characteristic of the N'Dama.

b) Write a sentence explaining why the amount of milk and meat they produce is less important.

c) Some less resistant breeds can be used. What do they need to help them survive?

d) Write down two problems with having to rely on drugs to protect the cattle.

e) (Difficult) "The N'Dama have a high level of genetic diversity." This means that they are quite varied — the cattle are less alike than Friesians. Write a sentence explaining why this would make it easier to produce cattle with a desired characteristic.

Lower the Sirloins — the steaks are too high...

How much wood would a woodchuck chuck if a woodchuck could chuck wood? Four tonnes, but with selective breeding it could be a lot more. You need to know how to explain different selected characteristics — eg why cows have been bred to be a certain way. Learn the examples, move on.

Selective Breeding — Plants

Q1 Copy out these sentences in the correct order to describe sexual reproduction in a flowering plant.

Fertilisation is complete.

The pollen cell nucleus travels down the tube.

The fertilised ovule becomes a seed.

Pollination is complete.

Pollen is taken from the anther by insects or the wind.

Some pollen grains reach a stigma in another plant.

Pollen is made in an anther.

This grows down through the carpel and into the ovule.

The pollen cell nucleus joins with the ovum.

The pollen grain germinates and grows a pollen tube.

Q2 Simon is a plant breeder who is producing new varieties of strawberry plant. He would like to produce the characteristics listed A to E below. The reasons for these characteristics are listed 1 to 5. Write down each characteristic with the reason that goes with it.

A plants are resistant to cold
B the fruit has a bright, even colour
C the fruit is sweeter
D the fruit will stay fresh longer
E there is more fruit on each plant

1 it will taste better
2 it will last longer in the shops
3 the grower will make more profit per acre
4 the growing season will be longer
5 it will be more attractive to shoppers

Q3 Artificial pollination can be carried out for lots of different reasons.

a) Write down which of the following statements is the reason for **selective** pollination.

- to make sure all flowers are pollinated
- to increase the amount of pollen reaching each stigma
- to control which plants are allowed to pollinate
- to replace the natural pollinators if they are not there

b) Selective pollination is practised for many different types of plant on a large scale in agriculture or small scale for amateur growers of specialised plants. Below are things which might be done by different growers. Write down each action and a reason for it to be done.

- cover shoots with buds on before flowers open
- collect pollen on a paint brush
- remove male plants before the flowers open
- plant only female plants in an area

This is such demeaning work for a shark robot. I used to be a Bond baddy you know.

Selective Breeding — Plants

Q1 Dionne and Jessica's class have been asked to investigate three varieties of garden pea to see which is the 'best'.

a) Write down three ideas for characteristics the girls could investigate.

b) The teacher asks them whether they would use 5, 50 or 5000 peas for their sample. Write down which you would use and why you wouldn't use the other two numbers.

c) They decide to investigate the diameter of the peas. The graph below shows their results.

Use the graph to copy and complete the sentences using the words below. You can use each word **once**, **more than once** or **not at all**.

smaller, larger, always, mostly, never

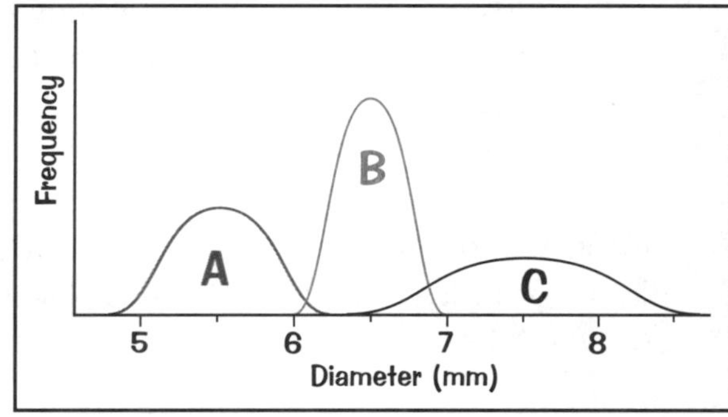

i) Peas of variety A are .... than those of variety B.

ii) Peas of variety A are .... than those of variety C.

iii) Peas of variety B are .... than those of variety C.

iv) Peas of variety C are .... than those of variety A and are .... than those of variety B.

Q2 Lynn and Sue decided to investigate cooking time. They put their samples in three beakers of boiling water and started timing. They were going to test a pea from each sample every two minutes to see if it was cooked. Write down three things they should do to keep it fair.

Q3 The class results are shown in the table below.

a) The class agreed that taste was the most important factor. Write down the letter of the pea with the best taste.

Test	Variety A	Variety B	Variety C
Average diameter (mm)	5.5	6.5	7.5
Average mass (mg)	51	83	129
Colour	Bright green	Pale green	Bright green
Taste (% who preferred it)	25	37	38
Cooking time (minutes)	16	18	22

b) The teacher asked then if they were sure that this was the best overall. Write down two reasons why there might be a different choice for best pea.

Forget the peas — grow me bigger chips and egg...

Don't get this selective breeding stuff mixed up with genetic modification (GM). GM plants are a whole different kettle of fish — they aren't bred at all, they're produced by altering genes directly.

Inheritance and Cloning

Q1 Copy and complete this paragraph.

Clones are individuals who are genetically [identical / different]. A clone is produced by [sexual / asexual] reproduction. Cloning has been carried out with [plants / humans] for many years. Variation in adult clones will still happen because of [environmental / genetic] factors.

Q2 Copy out the statements below that are **true**.

a) Cloning was first done in 1999.

b) There is no evidence that cloned animals suffer from health problems.

c) Cuttings taken from a plant are clones.

d) For every cloned animal that survives, many do not.

Q3 Answer the following questions.

a) Write down one characteristic you have which is **inherited** and one characteristic you have which is **environmental**.

b) Write a sentence to explain what is meant by the word **fertilisation**. (Include the word **nucleus**.)

c) Copy and complete these sentences:-

i) Sexual reproduction results in offspring which are genetically .... but not .... to the parents.

ii) Asexual reproduction results in offspring which are genetically .... to the ....

iii) .... factors can cause .... even in genetically identical individuals.

iv) .... breeding is used to produce desirable characteristics in animals and plants.

d) What 'F' follows pollination?

e) What 'V' is the word for differences between individuals?

f) What 'N' is where genetic information is found?

g) What 'C' is the female part of a flower?

h) What 'S' does a fertilised ovule become?

i) What 'G' is the word for a piece of genetic information?

j) What 'T' is an important adaptation for a sperm?

2000 years from now the first plant will become conscious and declare war on the human race. They will send a robot killer back in time to take out the ancestor of the human resistance leader.
The robot's name: The Pollinator
The target: Alan Titchmarsh

Fitness

Q1 Which of the following parts of the body would be affected by a consistently bad diet?

A) digestive system
B) respiratory system
C) circulatory system
D) skeleton and joints
E) all of the above, A-D

Q2 True or False? *"Fitness is a loose term that means different things to different people."*

Q3 Imagine you have to give a talk about how to keep fit.
Name three aspects of fitness you might discuss.

Q4 Copy and complete the sentences, choosing the right words.

Different people have different / similar levels of fitness. You can test this out yourself in class. Everybody should use a stopwatch to measure their temperature / pulse rate and then run on the spot for thirty seconds. They should measure it again at one minute intervals for the next five minutes. People who don't do much exercise will probably find it returns to normal fairly quickly / slowly. People who do lots of exercise will find it returns to normal fairly quickly / slowly.

Q5 Try and find an example of advice about fitness. You could look in magazines, newspapers, leisure centres or on the Internet.

Q6 Copy the diagram and label the arrows. Use the words in the box below.

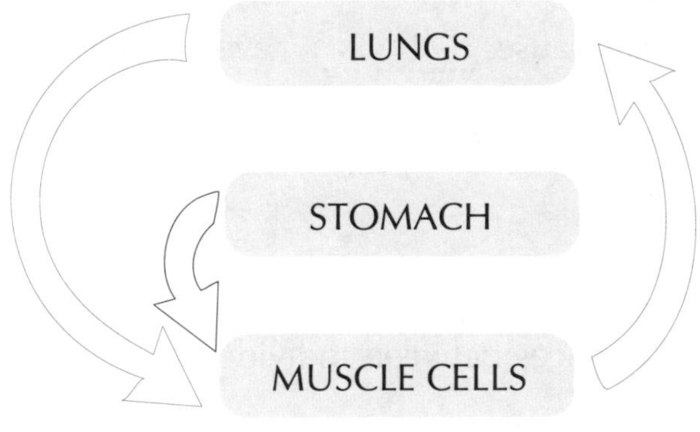

oxygen carbon dioxide glucose

Q7 Copy and complete the word equation for the reaction of respiration.

oxygen + ________ → carbon dioxide + ________ + energy

How the Respiratory System Works

Q1 Answer these questions about breathing.

a) Which organs are involved in breathing?

b) Which bone structure is involved in breathing?

c) Which muscles control breathing?

d) What is the name of the tubes through which air flows when you breathe?

e) Which gas is absorbed into the blood?

f) Which two substances are there more of in air breathed out than air breathed in?

Q2 Answer these questions about the actual **process** of breathing.

a) When you breathe in, what happens to the rib cage?

b) When you breathe out, what happens to the rib cage?

c) What happens to the volume of your chest when you breathe in?

d) What happens to the volume of your chest when you breathe out?

Q3 Sketch out this diagram, and label parts **A** to **G**.

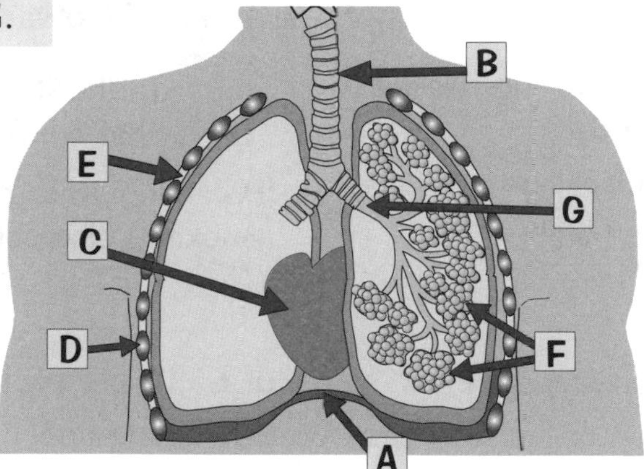

Q4 Which **one** of the statements below is true?

A Sucking in air causes the volume of your chest to increase.

B When you lift your ribcage up and out it increases the volume of your chest, which causes air to be sucked in.

Q5 Is the volume of air that one person breathes in and out always the same? Explain your answer.

Q6 Give two examples of activities that might **increase** lung volume over a period of time.

The Effects of Smoking

Q1 Name three harmful substances found in tobacco smoke.

Q2 The tubes in the lung are lined with **mucus-producing cells**. The cells are covered in little hairs called **cilia**, which flap and wave to shift the mucus up and out of the lungs.

a) What happens to bits of dirt and bacteria that get caught in the mucus?

b) The heat of cigarette smoke and the tar in the smoke damage the cilia. What does this mean for the mucus in a smoker's lungs?

c) What common (annoying, noisy) side-effect of smoking does this cause?

Q3 Give three examples of how tobacco smoke damages the body. For each one, name the substances that cause the damage.

Q4 If a pregnant woman smokes, what harmful effects could this have on her baby?

Q5 Describe the effects that smoking has on the circulatory system.

Q6 Why do smokers find it hard to stop smoking, even if they know it can damage their health?

Q7 Read these bits of information, and answer the questions below.

120 000 people die from smoking-related diseases every year in the UK.

Treating smoking-related diseases costs the NHS £1.5 billion a year.

In the 1950s, it was discovered that smoking causes lung cancer.

Breathing other people's smoke (passive smoking) also causes disease.

a) What is passive smoking?

b) If a man smokes 10 cigarettes a day, at a cost of £4.10 per pack of 20, how much money could he save each year by giving up?

c) Why do you think it's much rarer to see people smoking on TV and in films than it was 40 or 50 years ago?

d) Why is there a lot of tax on cigarettes? (i.e. Why does a lot of money from the sale of cigarettes go to the Government?)

Q8 What information would you give to people to persuade them that smoking is dangerous to health? Which information do you think is most important?

Effects of smoking — disease, debt, death and dog-breath...

On top of all the life-threatening diseases smoking gives you, it stinks. It really smells bad, and it's dead expensive. I mean, there are lots of cheaper ways to stink — rolling in cowpats is free.

The Importance of Diet

Q1 What nutrients make up a balanced diet?

Look at work from the Food and Digestion topic 8A in Book 2 to remind you.

Q2 What are the effects of not getting enough of each of these vitamins and minerals?

a) vitamin C

b) vitamin A

c) vitamin D

d) calcium

Q3 Describe the effects of **protein** deficiency on the body's appearance.

Q4 Describe how each of the following unhealthy diets affect the body.

a) a diet with too much fat

b) a diet with not enough fresh fruit and vegetables

c) a diet with too much sodium (too much salty food)

Q5 For each diet below, list 3 effects that eating them would have on a person's health and lifestyle.

a) Crisps and chocolate bars for breakfast; a packet of sweets in between classes; burger, chips and fizzy drink for lunch; some cake after school; a takeaway meal and more fizzy drink for dinner.

b) Nothing for breakfast; an apple for lunch, half a diet meal for dinner.

Q6 We know about the need for various nutrients in our diet because of research that has been done, and evidence that has been collected.

a) In the early 20th century, it was discovered that sufferers of a disease called pellagra ate mainly cornmeal. Cornmeal is low in vitamin B3. What's your conclusion about pellagra?

b) In an experiment, rats were given an artificial milk containing all the proteins, carbohydrates and fat they needed. They failed to grow. Why? What was missing?

How Alcohol Affects the Body

Q1 Answer the following questions about alcohol.

a) At what age can you drink alcohol legally?

b) Can too much alcohol kill you?

c) Why is it dangerous to drive after drinking alcohol?

d) Does alcohol alter the ability to make sensible choices and decisions?

e) Is alcohol a depressant (slows the brain down) or a stimulant (speeds the brain up)?

f) Is the amount of alcohol a person can drink a good way of measuring how "hard" they are?

Q2 Which large organ of the body is damaged by excessive drinking of alcohol?

Q3 Which of the following statements are **true**, and which are **false**?

A Alcohol is a poison.

B Alcohol speeds up your reactions.

C Alcohol is addictive.

Q4 Why are pregnant women advised to avoid drinking alcohol?

Q5 Answer these questions about the recommended maximum weekly alcohol consumption.

a) Why is there such a thing as a recommended maximum weekly amount of alcohol?

b) What are the current maximum amounts for i) men and ii) women?

c) Why are the amounts for men and women different?

d) Is it OK to drink your weekly amount all on one night and have no alcohol for the rest of the week? Why/why not?

Q6 Why do you think that hospital accident and emergency departments get very busy on Friday and Saturday nights?

Like a comedian — I can do without booze...

Alcohol is legal for adults to drink, and it can be enjoyed in moderation by most people. It is a drug though and it can ruin lives. You need to know what it does to the brain and the body.

Maintaining Fitness

Q1 A healthy heart is essential to keep everything else going.
How do the following things affect the health of the heart?

Some of these are good things, some are bad things.

a) A fatty diet.

b) Too much salt in the diet.

c) Taking exercise every day — enough to get you a little out of breath.

d) Smoking.

e) Drinking too much alcohol.

Q2 Exercise is great, but it can cause problems if you do it too vigorously.
Name one tissue of the body that can be damaged by sporting injuries.

Q3 What two things can you do before exercise to help prevent damage to the body?

Q4 Look at the diagram of a knee joint, and answer the questions below.

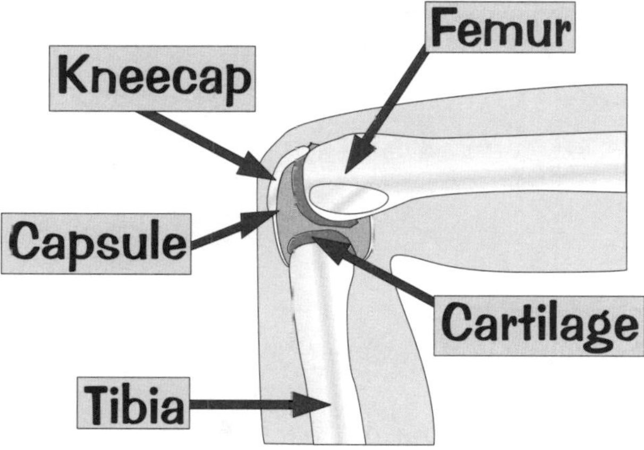

a) Which part of the joint is worn down by general wear and tear?

b) The shoulder joint is a ball and socket joint like the knee. Tennis players can injure the muscles and tendons around their shoulder joint when serving the ball hard. What kind of exercise should they do to prevent this kind of injury?

Q5 Severely damaged joints can be replaced by artificial joints.

a) What characteristics would materials for a hip replacement need to have?

b) Make a concept map of the design and testing of a hip replacement joint, and mark on the different stages of research, and some of the scientists and engineers involved.

The Effects of Drugs

Q1 Copy out this list of substances. By each one, write "drug" if it's a drug, or "not" if it's not a drug.

a) Paracetamol
b) Alcohol
c) TCP
d) Caffeine
e) Tea tree oil
f) Ampicillin (an antibiotic)
g) Cocaine
h) Cannabis

Q2 Give a definition of the term **drug**.

Q3 Copy out the diagram, and put the **drugs** from Q1 into the right place in each of the labelled circles.

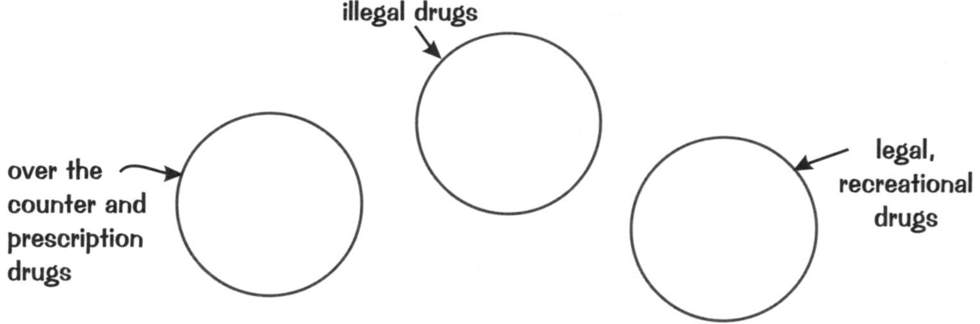

Q4 What is a **side-effect**?

Q5 Read about the experiment and answer the questions.

An investigation into the effects of caffeine on reaction time.
One group was given 100ml of caffeinated cola, and another group was given 100ml of decaffeinated cola. Both groups had their reaction time measured by the dropped ruler test (a ruler, held at zero, was dropped, and the subject caught it immediately. The higher the number the ruler was caught at, the slower the reaction time).

a) Why was everyone given the same volume of cola?

b) A small minority of people are sensitive to caffeine. What should the people carrying out the experiment do first to make sure no one is harmed?

c) Is it possible for the subjects of the experiment to influence the results if they know whether they have been given caffeinated or decaffeinated cola?

d) Is it possible for the people carrying out the experiment to influence the results if they know who has been given the caffeinated cola?

Are We Healthier Nowadays?

Q1 How would you find out how long people lived, on average, 80 years ago? What resources could you look at?

Q2 How could you find out what people died of 80 years ago?

Q3 What kind of information would you need, to find out how many people were tobacco smokers 80 years ago?

Q4 What kind of information could you use, to find out about the **attitude** that people had to smoking in those days?

Q5 How could you go about comparing the average daily lifestyle then with now?

Q6 Using the resources suggested in Q5, answer the following questions.

a) Did people have the same amount of labour-saving devices around the house?

b) Did more people do manual work?

c) Did more people cycle to work?

Q7 What about diet — did people eat a healthy diet in those days? How might you find out?

Q8 What medical advances have happened in the last 80 years? Which are most important?

Q9 What about babies and pregnancy? Did women have more kids? Did they all live?

Life — a sexually transmitted condition with 100% mortality...

There's two ways to find out about life eighty years ago 1) research, 2) build a time machine, go back eighty years and snoop about (trying not to kill any of your ancestors while you're there). Since Jonny Depp's got the time machine you're gonna have to stick with research I'm afraid.

How Plants Grow

Q1 Which of these statements are correct?
Only write out the true ones

a) Plants absorb food from the soil.

b) Plants need healthy leaves in order to grow.

c) Plants make food using oxygen from the air and minerals from the soil.

d) Plants make food using carbon dioxide from the air, and water from the soil.

e) Plants don't take in any food from the outside.

f) Plants need soil in order to grow.

Q2 Answer the questions on plant food production below.

a) What's the name of the process used by plants to make food?

b) What food substance is made by plants?

c) What two raw materials (ingredients) are used by plants to make this food?

d) In what form is this food stored?

Q3 As well as the two raw materials, what **three** other things do plants need to make food and grow?

Q4 Write out the word equation for photosynthesis.
Use some of the words from the box below, but not all of them.

Q5 The concentration of carbon dioxide around a tree is lower during the day than it is at night time. Why might this be?

Q6 Answer the questions on biomass below.

a) What is biomass?

b) Where does new plant biomass come from?

The Role of the Leaf

Q1 A green leaf was boiled in **water**, then boiled in **ethanol**. The leaf went **white**. The leaf was washed off with water, and a few drops of brown **iodine** solution were dropped onto the leaf. The leaf went **bluish black**.

a) Why was the leaf boiled in water?

b) Why was the leaf boiled in ethanol?

c) What colour do you think the ethanol went?

d) Why did the leaf turn blue-black when iodine was added?

Q2 The experiment in Q1 was carried out again with a green leaf that had been in the dark for 3 days. What would you expect to happen?

Q3 Read about this experiment, then answer the questions.

A green plant was kept in the dark for a couple of days. One of its leaves was covered with a piece of paper. The piece of paper had a circle cut out in the middle. It was taped tightly to the leaf so that light could only get to the bit of the leaf under the cut out circle. After a day in the sunshine, the leaf was tested for starch.

a) When iodine was dropped on the leaf, where would you expect the leaf to go black?

b) Why was the leaf kept in the dark for a couple of days before the experiment?

Q4 What pattern would you expect to see when a variegated green and white leaf is tested for starch?

Q5 Answer the questions on pigment in plants below.

a) What is the name of the green pigment in leaves?

b) Is this pigment necessary for photosynthesis? What's the evidence?

Q6 Answer the questions on plant health below.

a) What do plants look like when they've been kept in the dark for several days?

b) For big bonus points, what's the fancy scientific name for what happens to the plants?

You need to learn this — leaf it out at your peril... (I bet you'll be laughing yourself to sleep over that one tonight.)

There's only one real way to test if you know it. Do the questions. If you get them wrong, or you're stumped for the answer, look back at your class notes, and give them another go. Simple.

Leaves and Photosynthesis

Q1 What gas is produced during photosynthesis?

Q2 Read about the experiment, and answer the questions.

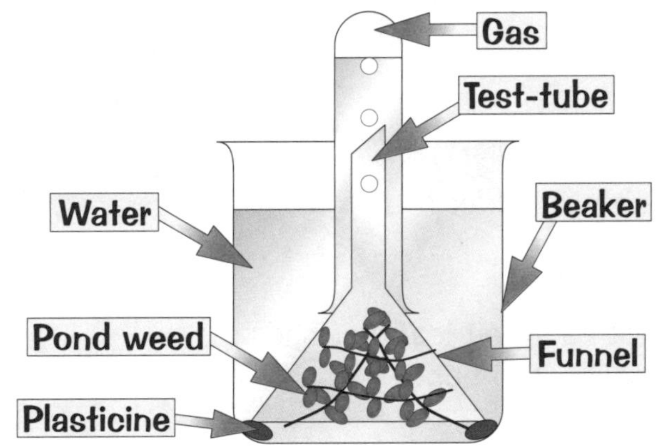

This is pondweed, which lives and photosynthesises underwater. A light was shone on the plant, and the bubbles made by the plant were collected in the test-tube.

a) Which gas do you expect to find in the test tube?

b) What is the lab test for this gas?

c) How might you measure the **rate** of pondweed photosynthesis?

Q3 Copy and complete the following sentence to explain what the gas produced by pondweed is used for.

.... produced by plants is used by plants and animals for .... which is the process that gets energy from glucose. .... produced by this process is used by plants for ....

Q4 Look at this cross-section diagram of cells in a leaf. Name three ways in which the top layers of cells are adapted for photosynthesis.

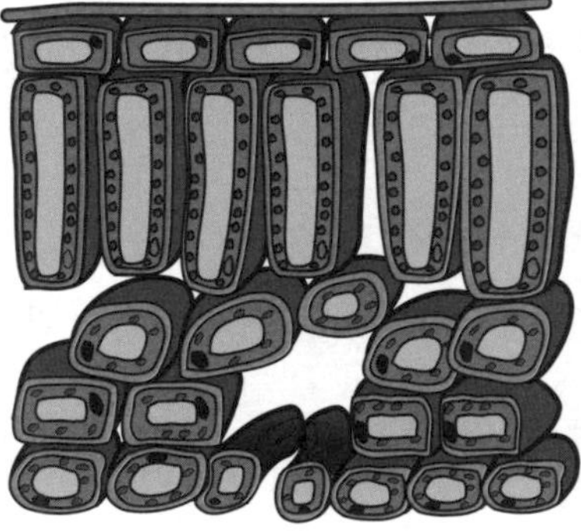

Q5 Give a definition of photosynthesis.

What Happens to the Glucose

Q1 What is the glucose created in photosynthesis stored as?

Q2 Some of the glucose made by photosynthesis is used by the plant straight away. What for?

Q3 Name five different foods which contain sugar or starch, and for each one, say whether they are **mainly sugar** or **mainly starch**.

Q4 Which of the statements below are **true** and which are **false**?

A Plants store glucose as starch in the roots, stems and leaves.

B As well as glucose, plants produce carbon dioxide through photosynthesis.

C Some glucose is used for plant respiration.

Q5 What substances do each of these plant products contain? Use the list in the box on the right to help you.

a) sunflower oil

b) potato flour

c) cotton

d) quorn

e) cane sugar

f) brazil nuts

g) bamboo canes

h) jute sack cloth

i) chick pea flour (gram flour)

cellulose, fat, starch, sugar, protein

Q6 Where do all the different substances in plant biomass come from?

Can you get quorn on the quob...

Not only do plants make their own sugar, but they manage to turn that sugar into every other substance that makes up their biomass. It's most impressive. They're no good at frisbee though.

The Role of the Root

Q1 Name three functions of roots.

Q2 Suggest a reason why waterlogged plants can die.

Q3 Name **three** ways that roots are adapted for their functions.

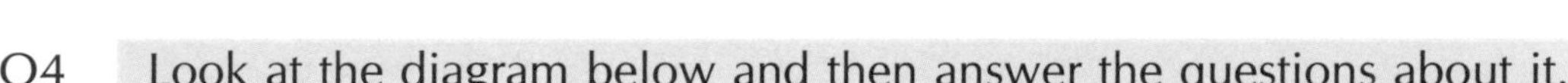

Q4 Look at the diagram below and then answer the questions about it.

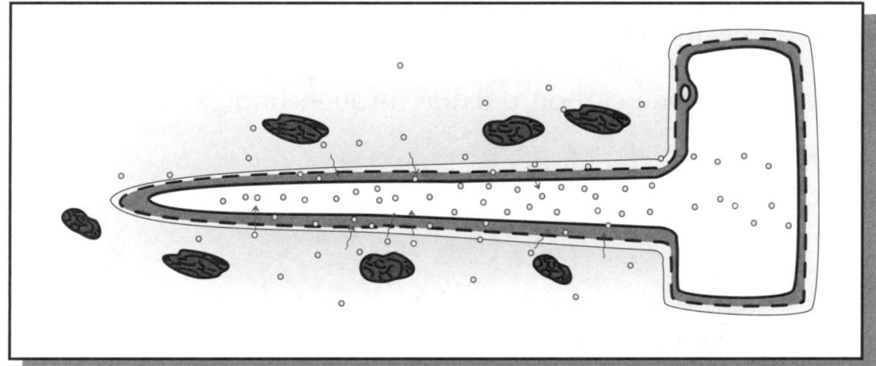

a) What kind of cell is this?

b) Name one way that this cell is adapted to its function.

Q5 How do substances taken in from the soil move through the plant?

Q6 A stick of celery, complete with leaves, was placed in a beaker of diluted ink. Say what you would expect to see after an day, and explain why.

Q7 All proteins contain **nitrogen**. Answer these questions about how plants make protein.

a) Where do plants get the nitrogen they need to make protein?

b) In what form do plants get the nitrogen they need — as nitrates, as nitrogen gas, or as nitrogen dioxide?

Q8 What is the purpose of fertiliser?

Green Plants in the Environment

Q1 Name the gases that are used and produced by:

a) photosynthesis.

b) respiration.

Q2 Imagine that the number of green plants on the Earth were drastically reduced.

a) What would happen to the concentration of oxygen in the atmosphere?

b) What would happen to the concentration of carbon dioxide in the atmosphere?

c) What would this mean for animal life, and why?

d) Explain how photosynthesis and respiration keep up the balance of gases in the air.

Q3 Read the following pieces of information. Make a list of advantages of cutting down forest, and a list of disadvantages of cutting down forest.

Green Ecological Institute Report
Carbon dioxide is a greenhouse gas. Increasing the amount of carbon dioxide in the atmosphere will make global warming worse. Trees use up carbon dioxide, so it's vitally important that we keep the trees!

Economic Development Bureau Bulletin
We need to grow more cash crops like coffee to sell in the global market and make money. Our country needs to repay its debts and start to become wealthy. We recommend cutting down forests and planting cash crops to achieve the best results for our economy.

Meat-o-rama Needs Land!
Demand for delicious MEAT is at an all-time high. We need more grazing land so we can raise more beef cattle. We'd pay big bucks ($$$!) for land cleared of trees.

Medical Research Group
We have recently discovered that some forest plants have amazing medical properties. We might be able to use compounds from these plants in medicines. The forests must be preserved until we finish our research.

Q4 Draw a rough diagram of a tree. Add labelled arrows to show the following:

a) Carbon dioxide entering the leaf

b) Oxygen going from the leaf into the atmosphere

c) Water entering the plant through the roots

Save our trees — don't use paper... Doh!

Here's one of those hot topics that people get worked up about. There are several sides to the issue, and you're expected to know them. Oh, and learn about the gases and water, too.

Where Our Food Comes From

Q1 Write out a food chain for each of these foods.

a) lamb chops

Milk is cow biomass. Milk doesn't eat cows. Think before you do your arrows.

b) milk

c) peaches

d) bread (just do a food chain for flour)

e) chips (do separate food chains for potatoes and sunflower oil)

f) carrot cake (do separate food chains for carrots, butter, sugar, flour and egg)

g) pork sausage (do separate food chains for pork meat and breadcrumbs)

For the purposes of this exercise, let's say that chickens eat grain, and pigs eat cooked chicken meat, potato and onion. Pigs actually eat "swill" which is leftovers from our food that gets cooked at 93° for two hours to kill any germs. Yum. Don't you wish you were a piggie now, eh...

Q2 For each of these food chains, name the producer.

a) algae → bugs → little fish → salmon

b) grass → cow → me

c) wheat → me

Q3 Which part of the plant are each of these foods (e.g. leaf, stem etc)?

a) cherry
b) carrot
c) brazil nut
d) cabbage
e) cornflour (ground maize)
f) rhubarb
g) potato
h) courgette
i) banana
j) pea
k) celery
l) onion

Q4 Write out the word equation for respiration. Do plants respire?

Q5 For each part of a plant shown below, suggest why a plant might store starch there.

a) the seed

b) the stem

c) the roots

Q6 Which vegetables are harvested in winter — leaf vegetables or root vegetables? Why do you think this is? Think about sunlight, starch storage, and the plant's needs.

How Fertilisers Affect Plant Growth

Q1 Look at these fertiliser labels. Based on the information they contain, which three elements are most needed by plants for healthy growth?

NPK fertiliser
NH_4NO_3
P_2O_5
K_2O

House plant food
NPK fertiliser
Percentage analysis by weight:

Total nitrogen	6%
Phosphorus pentoxide	6% (P 2.6%)
Potassium oxide	6% (K 4.9%)
Boron	0.012%
Copper	0.004%
Iron	0.04%
Manganese	0.02%
Molybdenum	0.0016%

Q2 How do the minerals in fertiliser get into the plant?

Q3 In what way can the use of fertiliser damage the environment?

Q4 Read about this experiment and answer the questions below.

Hyacinth bulbs were set up over four beakers of water, A-D. Each beaker had a different combination of nutrients in the water. The growth of the stems, roots and leaves was observed over the next week. The results are shown in this table:

Beaker	Minerals	Appearance of plants
A	nitrate, phosphate, potassium	Healthy roots and leaves
B	nitrate, potassium	Poor roots, leaves going purple
C	nitrate, phosphate	Yellow leaves with dead spots
D	phosphate, potassium	Yellow leaves, weak stems

a) What happens if nitrate is missing?

b) What happens if potassium is missing?

c) Which mineral is needed for healthy roots? How can you tell?

Q5 Imagine you are going to do an investigation into the effect of different fertilisers on the growth rate of wheat plants. Which variables can you control?

Q6 How would you make sure that variations in the starting size of the wheat plants didn't affect the results of your experiment?

Think numbers and averages...

What a load of fertiliser...

Fertilisers pack the soil with plenty of the minerals that plants need. If you don't know which minerals those are, then you need to give these questions another go. Go on, no time to lose...

How Competition Affects Plant Growth

Q1 *Plants living in the same environment* ***compete*** *with each other for resources.* Based on that nibble of information, give a definition of a **weed**.

Q2 What resources do weeds compete for?

Q3 How might animals be affected by the removal of a particular weed from their habitat?

Hint: think about food webs

Q4 Look at these weedkiller labels.

SuperStrong Systemic Weedkiller
Composition: Paraquat 53%
Handling Precautions: Avoid skin contact. Wear rubber gloves, boots, safety goggles and protective clothing. Do not inhale vapour. Wash hands after use. Wash contaminated clothing after use. Causes burns. Extremely toxic.
Storage precautions: Keep out of reach of children. Keep away from food,drink and animal feeding stuffs. Store between 0°C and 30°C. Keep container tightly closed. Keep only in the original container. Do not re-use container for any other purpose. Average shelf life 2 years.

Lawnation - Selective weedkiller, for control of broadleaved weeds in lawns. Active ingredient 2,4-D. Use caution to prevent spray solution contact with desirable broadleaf plants (flowers, vegetables, ornamentals, and shrubs). Do not spray on windy days. Wear protective gloves when mixing up solution. Do not dispose of unused solution into drains or watercourses.

a) What is a selective weedkiller?

b) Give a physical difference between leaf shape of grain crop plants and of most weeds.

c) Why do workers need to wear protective clothing while spraying SuperStrong?

d) Why is it important to keep weedkiller in its original container?

e) Why is it important to not reuse the container for anything else?

Q5 Suggest a way you could measure the population of weeds in a garden.

Q6 Imagine you want to measure how effective a particular weedkiller was at getting rid of weeds in a garden.

a) Write down a list of relevant variables in the experiment.

b) How would you control each of these variables, where possible?

c) Why should you have an untreated patch of land as a control?

d) What information would you use to help you decide how long to wait after weedkiller application before you measured the population of weeds again?

The Triffids — now those were killer weeds...

Nasty stuff, weedkiller. They seem to want you to know a little bit about how weedkillers are used. Don't forget the basic bits about what weeds do in terms of competition for resources.

How Pests Affect Plant Growth

Q1 Name an animal that competes with humans for each of these crops.

a) lettuce

b) wheat

c) cabbage

d) tomato

Q2 Draw a pyramid of numbers for each of the following feeding relationships.

a) An allotment of cabbages, about a hundred caterpillars eating the cabbages, and birds eating the caterpillars.

b) A field of wheat, mice eating the grains, and a barn owl hunting the mice.

c) A greenhouse full of tomato plants, a disgustingly large number of aphids on them, and a more decent number of ladybirds eating the aphids.

Q3 Give examples of methods used to control these pests.

a) slugs

b) aphids

c) locusts

Q4 Look at this food web and answer the questions

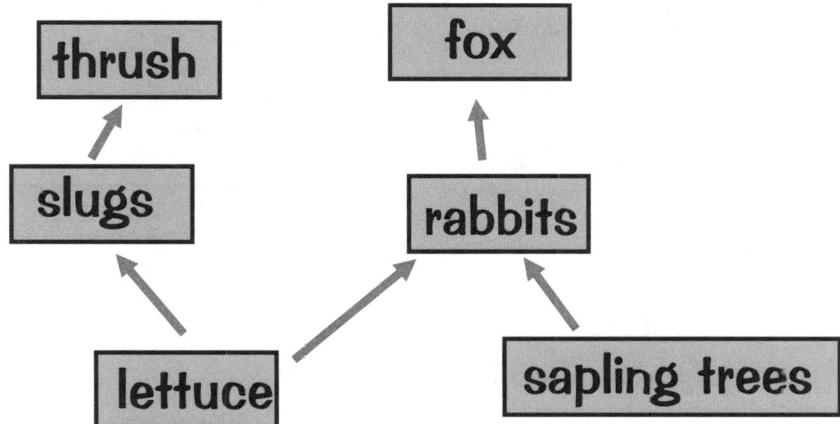

a) If the number of slugs decreased, what would happen to the number of thrushes?

b) What would happen to the number of foxes if some of the rabbits got killed?

c) If you drew a pyramid of numbers for the **lettuce — slugs — thrush** food chain, one for before putting down slug pellets, and one for afterwards, how would they be different?

Pesticide Pros and Cons

Q1 How might pesticides enter the food chain?

Q2 Toxic pesticide residues in an animal's body can either be excreted or they can build up.

a) If a mouse eats contaminated weeds, and doesn't excrete the toxins, what happens to the concentration of toxins in the animal's body, as time passes?

b) What about an owl that eats the mice — what would happen to the concentration of toxins in its body?

c) Which animals have the greatest concentration of toxins in their bodies — animals near the bottom of the food web, or animals at the top?

d) What's the fancy Biology name for what's going on here?

Q3 Read these snippets of information, and answer the questions below.

1) **DDT is the classic example of a pesticide that passed into the food chain with disastrous results.**
In a *phytoplankton - zooplankton - small fish - large fish - gull* food chain, the concentration of DDT in the gull's body was a staggering 200 000 times greater than in the phytoplankton.
Birds contaminated by DDT lay eggs with thin shells. In many cases, the shells are too thin to allow the chicks to survive.
Depleted populations of carnivorous birds have recovered since the banning of DDT.

2) It is essential to use pesticides to protect the food crops needed by the Earth's ever-growing population. A flock of locusts can wipe out an entire grain harvest in less than an hour.

3) Insecticides are the most toxic chemicals that the average person will encounter. They are all potent nerve agents, which attack the central nervous system of the pest insect, killing it. Insecticides will also attack the central nervous system of humans and other animals. Insecticides will remain active for many months if not years, providing a slow and steady dose of toxic chemicals to your body.

a) Briefly describe the point of view of the author of each text.

b) Do you think it's acceptable to use pesticides to produce more food for humans at the expense of other animal populations? Why/why not?

c) Do you think it depends on the pest and the environment in question? Why/why not?

Q4 Describe how pests are managed on organic farms.

Think about the predators that pests might have.

A Perfect Environment for Plants

Q1 Name five things that plants need to grow healthily.

Q2 Answer the questions below about growing plants.

a) What conditions is it possible to control when growing plants?

b) How might you control them?

Q3 Some food crops are grown in controlled environments inside greenhouses.

a) State two advantages of growing food crops this way.

b) State one disadvantage of growing food crops this way.

c) Why are most food crops not grown in greenhouses?

Q4 Answer the following questions about optimal conditions for plants.

a) Design a greenhouse with the perfect environment for crop production.

b) Label all control features, in each case explaining how they affect the environment.

Q5 Write two short paragraphs about the pros and cons of each of these farming systems:

a) Traditional crop farming, using chemical fertilisers, pesticides and weedkillers.

b) Organic farming, using no artificial chemicals at all.

Q6 Explain what is meant by the phrase below.

"sustainable development"

Perfect — pie shop, watching the World Cup with Kylie Minogue...

Sustainable development really is all the rage. You're expected to know a thing or two about the advantages and disadvantages of agricultural development. The most important thing to remember is that there's a balance of pros and cons. That's what makes it so tricky to decide...

Uses of Metals

Q1 Copy and complete the passage using the words in the grey box.

GOOD   ELECTRICAL CHARGE   THERMAL ENERGY   EASILY   POOR

All metals are .... conductors of heat and electricity;
they allow .... and .... to pass through them ....
Most non-metals are .... conductors of heat and electricity.

Q2 Use the words below to copy and complete the table. The first line has been done for you.

Electric wires, shiny, iron, lead, covering roofs, zinc.

Metal	A use	Property
Gold	Jewellery	It doesn't tarnish
	Hammer head	It is hard
Copper		Good electrical conductor
Silver	Candlesticks	
	Galvanizing	Stops iron rusting
		Easily beaten into shape

Q3 Below are lists of the electrical and thermal conductivities of some metal and non-metals:

Metal	Thermal Conductivity	Electrical Conductivity
Iron	80	99
Zinc	116	166
Copper	400	596
Lead	35	48
Gold	317	452
Silver	429	630
Non-metal	**Thermal Conductivity**	**Electrical Conductivity**
Sulfur	0	0
Oxygen	0	0
Graphite	129	6

a) Make one list of **all** the elements in order of electrical conductivity, starting with the best.

b) One of the non-metals is a conductor of electricity: which one?

c) Make a list of all the elements in order of their thermal conductivity, starting with the best.

d) Write a general rule for the electrical and thermal conductivities of metals and non-metals. Are there any exceptions to your rule?

Q4 Use a periodic table and your own knowledge to write a letter to someone on Mars explaining how useful metals are. Start by saying how many of the Earth's elements are metals.

Try to fit these words in:
hard, flexible, shiny, strong, conductors, heat, electricity, easy to shape.

Reactions between Metals and Acids

Q1 Copy and complete the passage using the words in the grey box. You can use the words more than once.

SALT DISSOLVES HYDROGEN GAS SQUEAKY POP

Some metals react with acids to produce bubbles of .... and a .... which usually .... in the acid. The .... can be tested by collecting it in a test tube and lighting it. If it is hydrogen, it will ignite with a ....

Q2 Copy and complete the word equations below showing the reactions of different metals with dilute acids. The first two have been done for you.

zinc + sulfuric acid ⟶ zinc sulfate + hydrogen

zinc + hydrochloric acid ⟶ zinc chloride + hydrogen

iron + sulfuric acid ⟶ .... + hydrogen

iron + hydrochloric acid ⟶ .... + hydrogen

magnesium + sulfuric acid ⟶ .... + hydrogen

.... + hydrochloric acid ⟶ magnesium chloride + hydrogen

.... + ... ⟶ calcium chloride + hydrogen

tin + ... ⟶ tin sulfate + hydrogen

tin + hydrochloric acid ⟶ tin chloride + ...

.... + sulfuric acid ⟶ lead sulfate + ...

.... + ... ⟶ lead chloride + ...

Q3 The first two equations in Q2 have been drawn below using circles to represent atoms in the reaction. **Now do the same with the rest of the equations in Q2.**

Word equation: zinc + sulfuric acid ⟶ zinc sulfate + hydrogen

Symbol equation: $Zn + H_2SO_4 \longrightarrow ZnSO_4 + H_2$

Word equation: zinc + hydrochloric acid ⟶ zinc chloride + hydrogen

Symbol equation: $Zn + 2HCl \longrightarrow ZnCl_2 + H_2$

Metal Carbonates

Q1 Copy and complete the passage using the words in the grey box.

ACID CHEMICAL REACTION CARBONATE WARMER
CARBON DIOXIDE SALT BUBBLES DISSOLVE

When a metal .... is put into an ...., a .... takes place. We know this because .... of .... gas are formed and the acid gets .... The carbonate forms a new salt that may .... in the acid.

Q2 Copy the diagram below and then do these questions.

a) Complete the missing label on the diagram.

b) What would you **see** happen to the limewater?

c) What is the name of the new salt formed in tube A?

d) What happens to this salt when it is formed?

e) Use the words below to copy and complete the word equation for this reaction in tube A.

Carbon dioxide, water, nitric acid, calcium nitrate, calcium carbonate.

.... + ... ⟶ .... + ... + ...

Q3 Below are some word equations for reactions between some dilute acids and metal carbonates. Copy the equations, filling in the missing words. The first two have been done for you.

a) lead carbonate + hydrochloric acid ⟶ lead chloride + carbon dioxide + water

b) iron carbonate + sulfuric acid ⟶ iron sulfate + carbon dioxide + water

c) tin carbonate + nitric acid ⟶ tin nitrate + ... + water

d) .... carbonate + nitric acid ⟶ zinc nitrate + carbon dioxide + ...

e) copper carbonate + sulfuric acid ⟶ .... + ... + water

f) magnesium carbonate + nitric acid ⟶ .... + ... + ...

g) .... carbonate + ... acid ⟶ iron nitrate + ... + ...

h) Write a **general** word equation for the reaction of a metal carbonate with an acid.

Use the words: water, metal carbonate, salt, acid, carbon dioxide.

.... + ... ⟶ .... + ... + ...

Acids and Metal Oxides

Q1 Look carefully at the diagram and then copy and complete the description of what is happening. Use the words in the grey box (you can use any of them more than once).

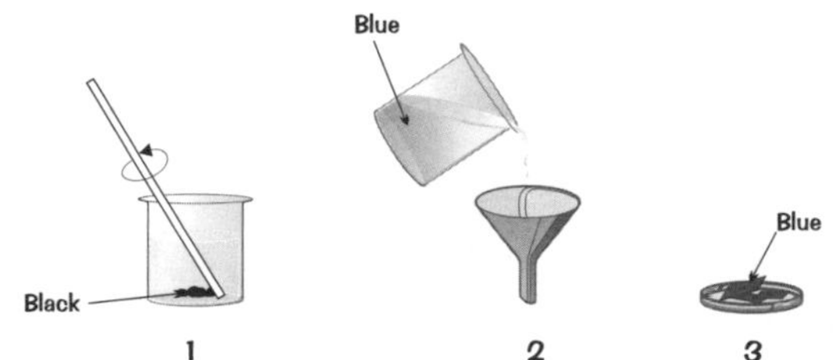

BLUE	COPPER SULFATE
BLACK	CHEMICAL REACTION
COLOURLESS	COPPER OXIDE

1) .... copper oxide powder is stirred into .... dilute sulfuric acid. The solution turns .... This colour change tells us a .... has happened.

2) When the .... solution is filtered, un-reacted black .... is left in the filter paper.

3) When the blue solution is left to evaporate, it leaves behind .... crystals of .... These crystals tell us a .... has happened.

Q2 Copy and complete the word equations for the reactions of some metal oxides with dilute acids. The first one has been done for you.

a) tin oxide + hydrochloric acid ⟶ tin chloride + water

b) zinc oxide + hydrochloric acid ⟶ .... + water

c) copper oxide + sulfuric acid ⟶ copper sulfate + ...

d) lead oxide + ... ⟶ lead sulfate + ...

e) .... + nitric acid ⟶ iron nitrate + water

f) .... + ... ⟶ magnesium nitrate + ...

g) Using the words below, copy and complete the **general** word equation to represent the reaction between **any** metal oxide and **any** dilute acid.

SALT   METAL OXIDE   WATER   A DILUTE ACID

.... + ... ⟶ .... + ...

Q3 Zinc oxide and zinc carbonate are both white powders.

a) Explain how you could use dilute sulfuric acid to tell them apart. You can use any normal laboratory equipment.

b) Write word equations for any reactions.

c) Write symbol equations for the word equations in b).

Cattle with iron backsides — metal ox-hides...

More equation-tastic questions than you can shake a metal oxide at. But the only way to get good at this stuff is to practise and practise — mumma said there'd be days like this.

Salts

Q1 Below are five beakers each containing 100 cm^3 of different solutions. Their pHs are shown on them.

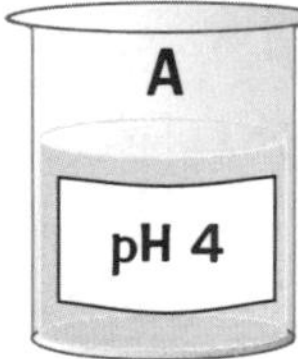

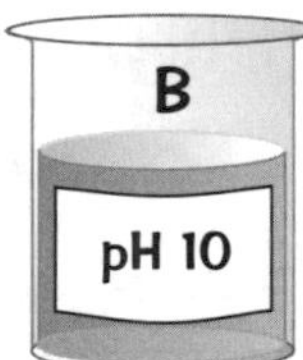

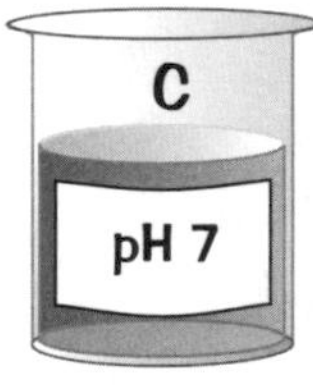

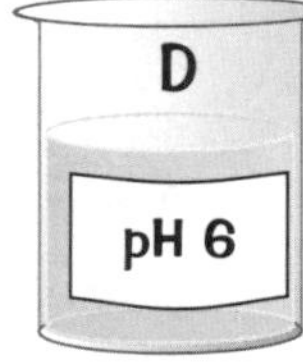

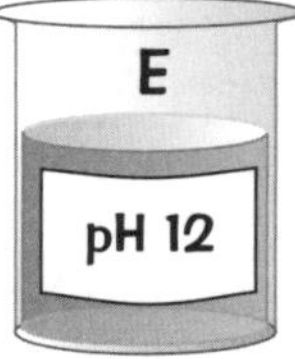

a) Which beaker contains a **neutral** solution?

b) Which beakers contain an **acid** solution?

c) Which beakers contain **alkaline** solutions?

d) Which two beakers could be mixed to produce a **neutral** solution?

Q2 You are given:

100 cm^3 of **sodium hydroxide solution, pH12**

100 cm^3 of **hydrochloric acid solution pH2**

Usual laboratory equipment.

a) How would you get a sample of common salt **(sodium chloride)** for your chips?

b) Write a word equation for any chemical reaction that takes place.

c) What is this **type** of chemical reaction called?

d) What safety precautions would you take?

Q3 You are given:

A bottle of **hydrochloric acid solution, pH unknown**.

A bottle of **potassium hydroxide solution, pH unknown.**

Some **universal indicator** solution and **a pH colour chart.**

Usual laboratory equipment.

a) How would you obtain a sample of the salt **potassium chloride**?

b) Write a word equation for any chemical reaction.

c) What safety precautions would you take?

Salts

Q1 Copy and complete the following word equations for neutralization reactions. The first three have been done for you.

a) calcium hydroxide + hydrochloric acid ⟶ calcium chloride + water

b) magnesium hydroxide + sulfuric acid ⟶ magnesium sulfate + water

c) silver hydroxide + nitric acid ⟶ silver nitrate + water

d) sodium hydroxide + hydrochloric acid ⟶ .... + water

e) potassium hydroxide + nitric acid ⟶ .... + water

f) iron hydroxide + sulfuric acid ⟶ .... + water

g) .... + nitric acid ⟶ magnesium nitrate + water

h) .... + ... ⟶ potassium nitrate + water

i) Use the following words to copy and complete the **general** equation for the neutralization of an acid and an alkali:

SALT, ALKALI, WATER, ACID.

.... + ... ⟶ .... + ...

No doubts

Q2 **Extension**. Below is a list of some useful salts. Use your class information folders and other sources to complete the table. Part of the first one has been done for you.

Salt	Use	How it could be made
Sodium stearate		Sodium hydroxide + stearic acid (in fat)
Potassium nitrate		
Copper sulfate		
Calcium phosphate		
Iron sulfate		
Magnesium sulfate		
Silver nitrate		

Salt & Water ⟶ pretty grim crisps...

You need to understand all these equations but remember the general one (in Q1. part i) and life will be a lot easier. You also need to remember how to make salts and don't forget the safety precautions. With all that to learn no wonder they say too much salt is bad for your heart.

Salts

Q1 Look at the apparatus below and answer the questions which follow.

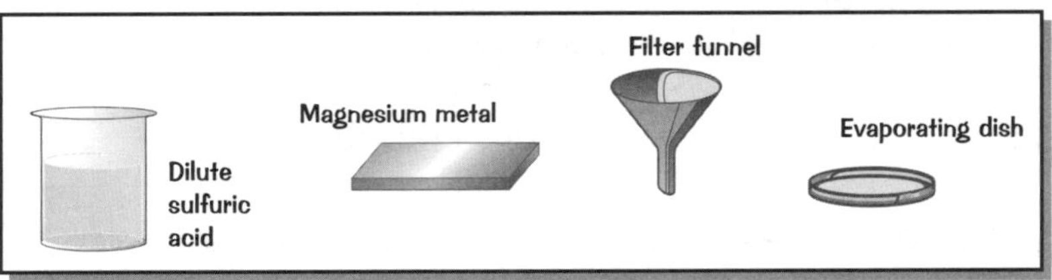

a) Using the apparatus and any other usual laboratory equipment, plan an experiment to make magnesium sulfate crystals. Include diagrams.

b) Write a word equation for any chemical reactions.
c) Say what safety measures you would take.

Q2 You are given a mixture of calcium sulfate and calcium carbonate powders.

> Calcium sulfate is a white powder that does **not dissolve** in water and does **not** react with acids.
>
> Calcium carbonate is a white powder that does **not** dissolve in water.

Given dilute hydrochloric acid and any other usual laboratory equipment:

a) Write a plan for an experiment to produce pure samples of the salts calcium sulfate and calcium chloride from the mixture.
b) Write word equations for any chemical reactions.
c) How could you test that no calcium carbonate remained in your sample of calcium chloride?
d) Say what safety precautions you would take.

Q3 In the experiment shown below the evaporating dish is found to contain blue crystals of copper nitrate but they are contaminated with particles of black copper oxide. **There is no nitric acid left.**

a) How could you separate the copper oxide from the copper nitrate crystals?
Hint: copper oxide is **not soluble** in water. **All** nitrates are **soluble** in water.
b) How would you modify the experiment above to produce more pure copper nitrate?

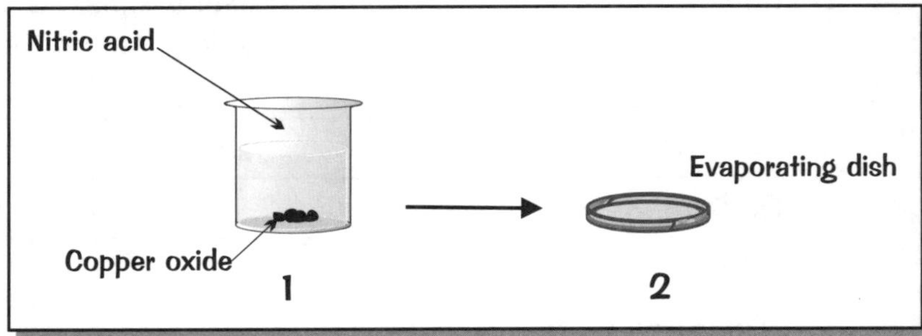

c) Write a word equation for any chemical reaction taking place.
d) Say what safety precautions you would use.

Q4 Two hundred years ago barrels of **sulfuric acid** and **iron** filings were used to fill gas balloons with **hydrogen** to take people on the first flights.

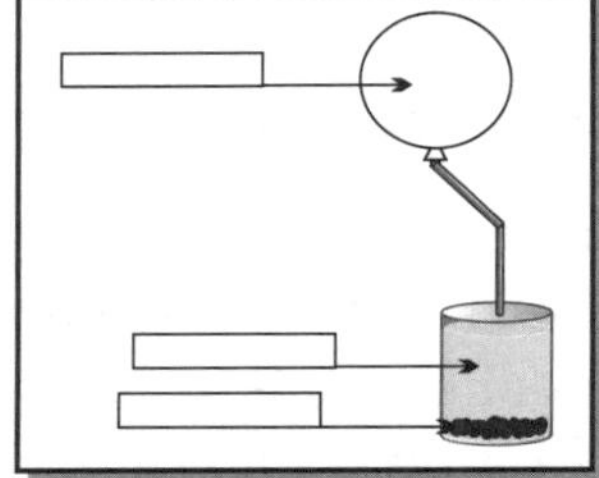

a) Copy the diagram and label it.
b) Write a word equation for the chemical reaction.
c) Green crystals were left in the barrel after the balloon was filled with hydrogen. What are the crystals? How did they get there? Is there any use for them?

Metals and Air

Q1 **The diagrams below show some metallic objects of different ages.**

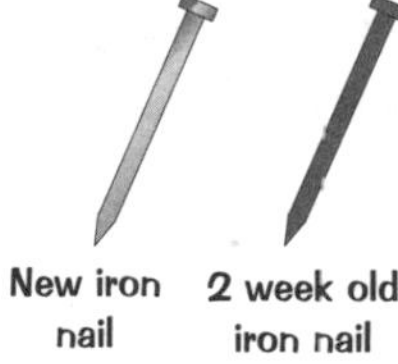

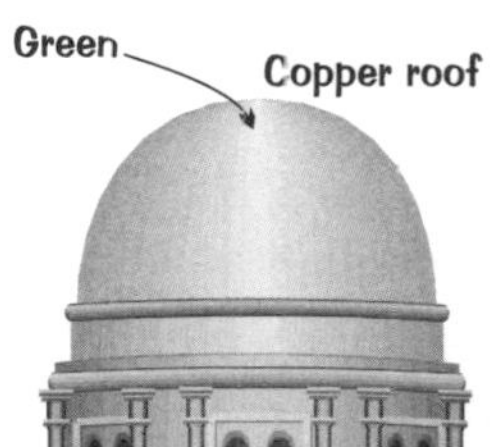

a) What effect does air and moisture have on the metals above?

b) Which metal does not seem to react with the air and moisture?

c) Why do you think that is?

d) Can this metal be worn next to the skin, without it reacting?

e) What would happen if iron was worn next to the skin for several months?

Q2 **A bayonet is a bit like a sword which solders put on the end of their rifles. The metal bayonet shown was found in a farmer's field and was thought to be about 85 years old.**

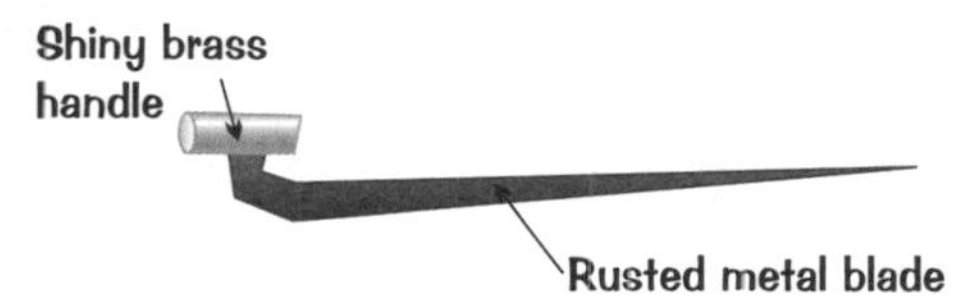

a) What do you think the blade is made out of?

b) What has the blade reacted with to produce the rust?

c) Why has the metal on the handle not reacted like the blade?

d) A local war museum had an identical bayonet which was shiny and looked almost new. Explain why there is a difference in the condition of the bayonets.

Q3 **Samples of sodium, potassium and lithium are shown to the right.**

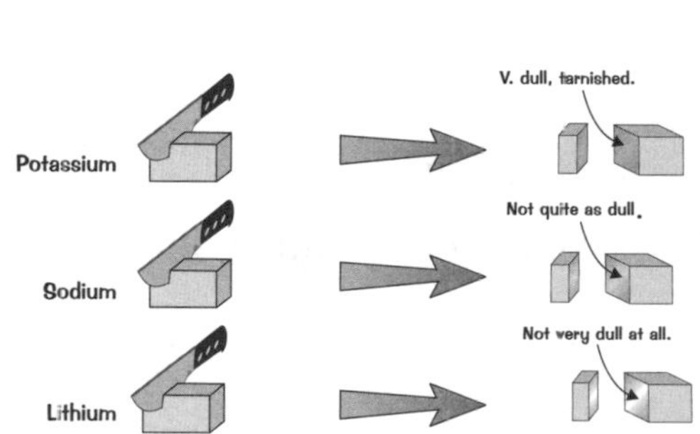

a) Where are these elements in the Periodic Table?

b) Are they metals or non-metals? Explain how you know.

c) List four other properties that these elements might have.

d) Which element would you expect to be the most reactive? Explain your answer.

e) What have the elements reacted with when they were cut and tarnished?

Metals Reacting with Water

Q1 Use these metals to answer the questions (there may be more than one answer per question).

Potassium | Copper | Iron | Sodium | Magnesium

a) Write down which of the metals react with cold water.

b) Which metals would tarnish quickly on exposure to air?

c) Which metals would tarnish slowly on exposure to air?

d) Put the metals in order of how easily they react with water and the air. (Put the most reactive metal first.)

Q2 The apparatus shown to the right was set up.

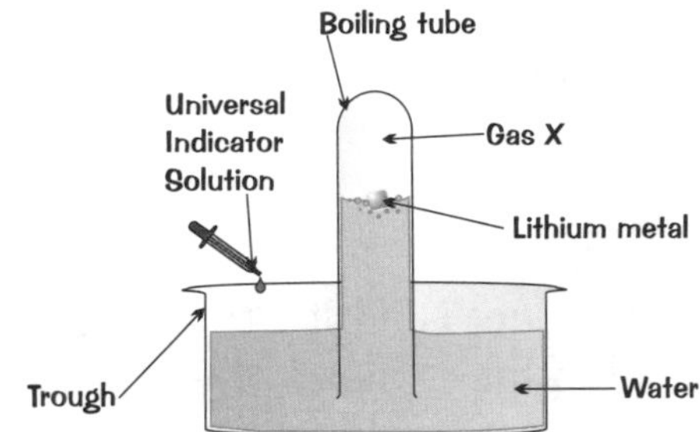

a) Describe what you would see.

b) Name gas X.

c) Describe a simple test to identify gas X.

d) If universal indicator solution was poured into the water, what would you see?

e) Explain why you would see this observation.

f) Write a word equation for the reaction.

g) If the reaction was repeated with sodium describe what you would see.

Q3 Copy and correct the bold words in the sentences below.

Potassium metal was put on water in a glass trough. The metal **sank** and then fizzed giving off **oxygen** gas. The reaction gave off so much heat that the metal **boiled** and the gas ignited to produce **an orange** flame. The reaction produced potassium **oxide**, which is alkaline and turns UI solution **red**.

Vauxhall's indicator solution — they get louder the faster you go...

It's the metals in group I of the Periodic Table that react with water. The reaction gets more vigorous as you go down the group. When you get down to rubidium and caesium you're in for some major excitement, let me tell you. Oh yes. Unfortunately, it's too dangerous to do in school, so you just have to watch the 70s video of the bearded bloke with the big collar doing it.

Metals and Acid

Q1 Acids can react with metals to produce two main products.

a) Name these two products.

b) Copy and complete the following word equation to show how metals react with acids

metal + acid → .... + ...

c) How could you test for the gas that is produced in this reaction?

Q2 Not all metals react in the same way. The table below shows how some metals react with hydrochloric acid.

Metal	Symbol	Reaction with acid	Observations
Copper		nothing seen	no bubbles
	Zn		quite a lot of bubbles
Iron		a moderate reaction seen	

a) Using the bold words and phrases below, copy and complete the table.

Cu **Zinc** **vigorous reaction** **Fe** **a few bubbles were seen**

b) Which do you think is the most reactive metal out of those given in the table?

c) Copper did not seem to react very well with the acid. Why do you think this is?

Q3 Complete the following:

a) Zinc + hydrochloric acid → .... + ...

b) Iron + hydrochloric acid → .... + ...

c) Copper + hydrochloric acid → ....

d) List the metals in the table in order of reactivity to hydrochloric acid.

e) How do you think the metals in the table would react with sulfuric acid?

f) If magnesium was reacted with hydrochloric acid, predict what the equation would be.

Magnesium + hydrochloric acid → .... + ...

Q4 Tin cans are usually made from steel which contains iron. The cans are lined with a thin layer of tin or sometimes plastic. Why do you think tinned fruit like mandarins could never be put in a steel can without some kind of coating?

Metals and Oxygen

Q1 Copy and complete the sentences below using the following words:

properties joining chemical reaction oxide

When a metal reacts with oxygen it forms a metal ....

This is a .... change or chemical .... which involves the metal chemically .... to oxygen. The compound which is made has different .... from the metal and the oxygen from which it was formed.

Q2 The diagram shows an experiment where different metals were reacted with air and oxygen. The results are shown in the table.

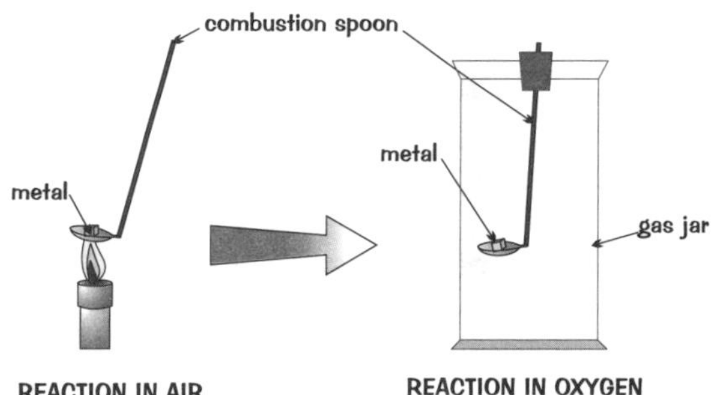

Metal	Reaction with Air	Reaction with Oxygen
Iron	Turns the flame orange. (Needed to be iron wool or powder to burn.)	Burns with an orange glow (with the iron wool or powder).
Magnesium	Burns and glows with a bright white flame, forms a white solid.	Burns and glows with sparks and a very bright white flame, forms a white solid.
Copper	Turns the flame green, forms a black layer on the copper.	Glows with a bright green flame, forms a black layer on copper.
Zinc	Glows red, a white material forms.	With powder, white and yellow sparks jump out of the combustion spoon.

a) Is there a difference in the way each metal reacts with air and oxygen? If so, describe it.

b) Why do you think this is?

c) By examining the results in the table, put the metals in order of reactivity, the most reactive metal first.

Q3 Complete the following equations

a) Iron + oxygen → ....

b) Magnesium + oxygen → ....

c) Copper + oxygen → ....

d) Zinc + oxygen → ....

Facts + brain = knowledge + fatigue...

Three lumps of knowledge to get into your head cavity — how different metals react with oxygen, what's formed from the reactions and how reactive the metals are. No problem.

Displacement Reactions

Q1 a) Copy the table below into your book.

Metal salt	Metal			
	Lead	Iron	Copper	Zinc
Zinc sulfate	No reaction	No reaction	No reaction	No reaction
Iron sulfate	No reaction	No reaction	No reaction	Grey metal deposited on the nail.
Copper sulfate	Orange/brown metal deposited on lead. Blue solution goes colourless.	Orange/brown metal deposited on nail. Blue solution goes colourless.	No reaction. Blue solution stays blue.	Orange/brown metal deposited on zinc. Blue solution goes colourless.
Silver nitrate	Shiny/grey metal deposited on lead.	Shiny/grey metal deposited on nail.	Shiny/grey metal deposited on copper.	Shiny/grey metal deposited on zinc.

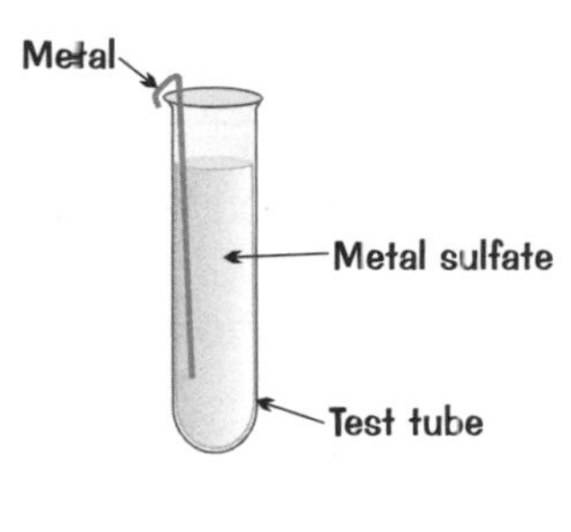

b) Write out word equations for all the reactions in the third line of the table.

i) copper sulfate + lead → .... + ...

ii) copper sulfate + iron → .... + ...

iii) copper sulfate + copper → ....

iv) copper sulfate + zinc → .... + ...

Q2 Alex was asked to use polystyrene balls and glue and cocktail sticks to show why some metals displace certain metals from their compounds but not others. His models are shown below:

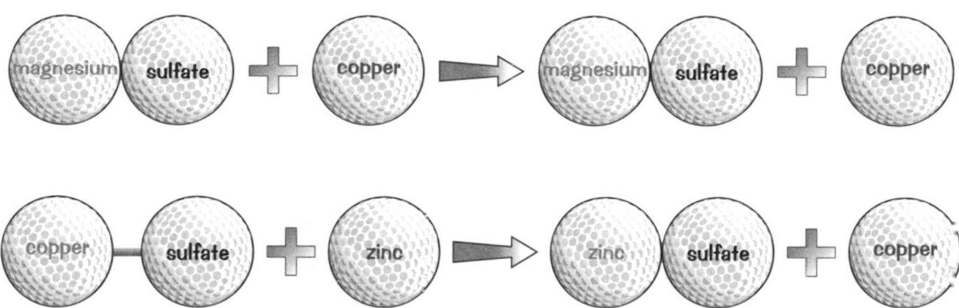

a) Explain what Alex's models are showing.

b) Which is most reactive i) magnesium or copper? ii) copper or zinc?

c) Why has he used a wooden cocktail stick for one molecule of a compound and strong glue for another?

d) What is the name given to this type of reaction?

Q3 "If a metal is high in the activity series it will displace or push out a metal which is lower in the series". Explain in as much detail as you can what this statement means.

Useful Displacement Reactions

Q1 The Thermit reaction is a reaction between iron (II) oxide and aluminium. It is often used in welding, for example where railway tracks need joining together.

The reaction is: iron (II) oxide + aluminium → aluminium oxide + iron

a) The reaction gives out lots of heat energy. What does this heat energy do to the iron?

b) Why do you think this is useful?

c) Why does the aluminium take the place of the iron in iron oxide?

d) Could this reaction be used to weld two pieces of aircraft body panels together which contain an alloy of magnesium and aluminium? Explain your answer.

Q2 The reactivity of a newly discovered metal called 'benhiddium' was investigated. The new metal was put with a number of substances as shown in the table.

Experiment	Metal	Metal compound	Observations
1	benhiddium	zinc sulfate	No reaction seen.
2	benhiddium	iron sulfate	Traces of grey material seen on benhiddium.
3	zinc	benhiddium sulfate	Lumps of silvery coloured substance seen on zinc.
4	iron	benhiddium sulfate	No reaction seen.

Now use the activity series opposite to answer these questions:

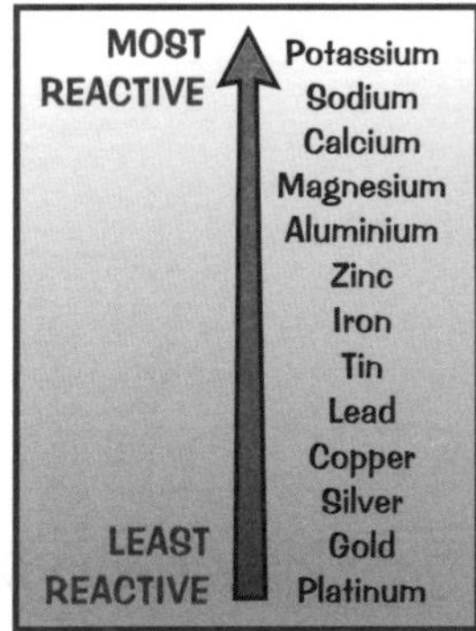

a) Does benhiddium react with zinc sulfate and iron sulfate?

b) Is benhiddium more reactive or less reactive than zinc?

c) Is benhiddium more reactive or less reactive than iron?

d) Do the last two reactions in the table agree with your answers to parts b) and c)?

e) Using the information in the table, write out the activity series with benhiddium in the correct position.

f) Write out word equations for experiments 1 to 4.

Hiddium, hiddium, hiddy um pum pum — yeeeee haaaa...

Your mission, should you choose to accept it: get to grips with the activity series. OK so it's not the kind of mission Tom Cruise gets, but he's not doing key stage three science is he.

Uses and Sources of Metals

Q1 To do this question you need to do look up information on these four elements.

sodium	iron	aluminium	gold

You could get this information from books, CD roms, videos or the internet. You'll need to find out where they occur, how they are extracted from their ores and what they are used for.

a) Where is each metal found in the world? Name one place for each metal.

b) In what form is each metal found? (e.g. as a metal chloride or an oxide?)

c) How much of each of them is in the Earth's crust?

d) When was each metal first discovered?

e) How do we extract each metal from its ore? (smelting with carbon, electrolysis, etc.)

f) What are the physical properties of each metal (e.g. melting point/density/tensile strength)?

g) Is each metal high or low in the activity series?

h) Is each metal above or below i) carbon ii) hydrogen?

i) What are the metals used for?

j) Are they ever mixed with other metals (alloyed) to alter their properties?

Q2 Is the method of extracting a metal from its ore linked to i) its reactivity ii) when it was first discovered?

Q3 Copy out the table below. Next to each of the metals write one of the following words:

Smelting	electrolysis	found a native metal	heating in air

Metal	How it is extracted
potassium	
sodium	
calcium	
magnesium	
aluminium	
zinc	
iron	
tin	
lead	
copper	
silver	
gold	
platinum	

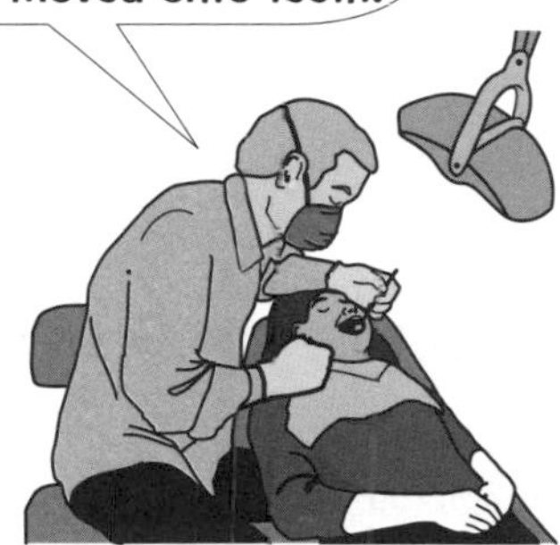

A Review of Patterns of Reactivity

Q1 Copy and complete the passage using these words.

displace higher activity smelting expensive

Different metals have different reactivities. This means that some metals react with certain things, some react, but slowly and others don't react at all. The more reactive a metal is the .... it is in the .... series. A metal high in the series will replace or .... a metal lower in the series. This principle is used to extract metals from their ores and is demonstrated when metals react with acids. Metals lower than carbon in the activity series, can be heated with carbon to extract the metal, this is called .... Metals lower than hydrogen in the series could be extracted using hydrogen gas, but this would be ....
Metals above hydrogen in the series can react with acids to make hydrogen gas.

Q2 Words in science have precise meanings, explain what the following mean by putting them into a suitable sentence.

a) compound
b) reactivity
c) react
d) salt
e) equation
f) reactant
g) product
h) copper sulfate
i) magnesium nitrate
j) zinc chloride
k) order of reactivity
l) qualitative observations

Q3 Powdered iron was heated with copper oxide as shown in the diagram below.

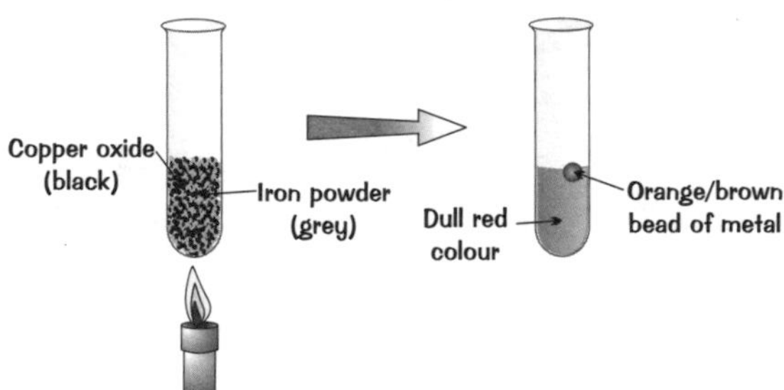

a) Describe what would you see happen in this reaction.

b) How do you know a chemical reaction has taken place?

c) Write out a word equation for this reaction.

Different Soils

Q1 A good soil has 6 important ingredients.

Solve each anagram to find them:

a) kcro seitprcal

b) seimranl

c) ari

d) inlvgi migoanrss

e) tawre

f) uumsh

A fine, fruity soil with hint of cow.

Q2 Write out the complete sentences by matching up the correct halves:

a) Sandy soil contains larger rock particles

b) Clay soil has little air in it

c) Plant roots hold soil together

d) Humus is dead organic matter in soil

e) Loam is an ideal soil type

f) Organisms like worms are vital for soil

- because it has good mineral content and drains well
- which provides nutrients
- because they help to circulate air
- so water drains through it quickly
- which helps to prevent erosion
- so few organisms can live in it

Q3 The pH range of most soils is between pH 4.5 and pH 7.5.
This part of the pH scale is shown below.

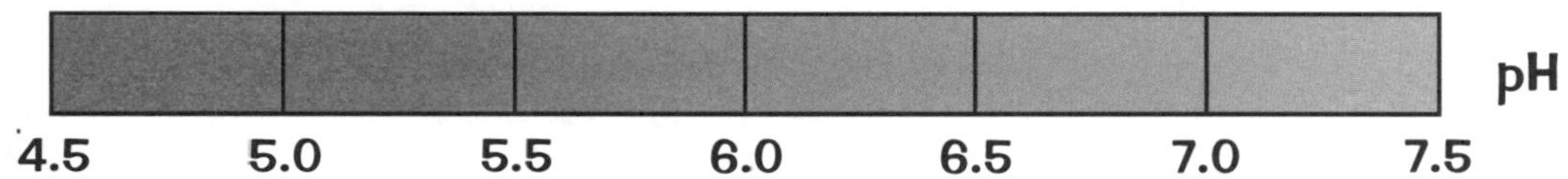

a) Copy and mark on the scale:
i) acid ii) alkali iii) neutral

b) Here are some vegetables and what type of soil they grow best in:

Carrot: pH 6	Potato: pH 5	Onion: pH 7

Sandy, a gardener, wants to grow onions.

He tested his garden soil with a pH meter and found it to be pH 4.5

i) Will Sandy need to **increase** or **decrease** the pH of his soil to grow onions well ?

ii) What type of substance will Sandy need to add to his soil to achieve this?

iii) What would be a better vegetable to grow in his garden ?

Acid Rain

Q1 A limestone wall on Holly's farm has been badly worn away.

Explain how damage is caused by **weathering** in each of the descriptions below.

a) Many trees grow alongside the wall.

b) In the winter, water collects in holes and cracks and freezes.

c) Jenny's wall lies across a popular public footpath and has a stile over it.

d) Jenny's farm is in an area which suffers from acid rain.

Q2 Rain water is naturally acidic due to the carbon dioxide gas in the air. Copy and complete the diagram, to explain how carbon dioxide gas produced by burning fossil fuels, results in rain water being weakly acidic.

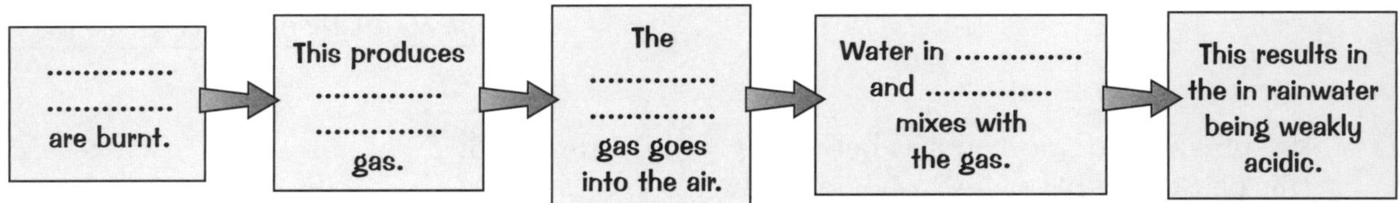

Q3 Acid rain is also caused by oxides of sulfur.

Suggest ways that oxides of sulfur can get into the atmosphere by:

a) human activity

b) geological activity

Acid raindrops keep falling on my head (causing quite an erosion problem)...

Acid rain is definitely a major cause of erosion of rocks and also statues and wot not. Mind you it's important that you don't forget that there are plenty of other types of erosion as well, like wind, and human activity... question one has some good reminders — remember.

The Effects of Acid Rain

Q1 Acid rain can wear away rocks and damage building materials.

Paula and Kate investigated how the laboratory acid, **nitric acid** affected 3 different rock types.

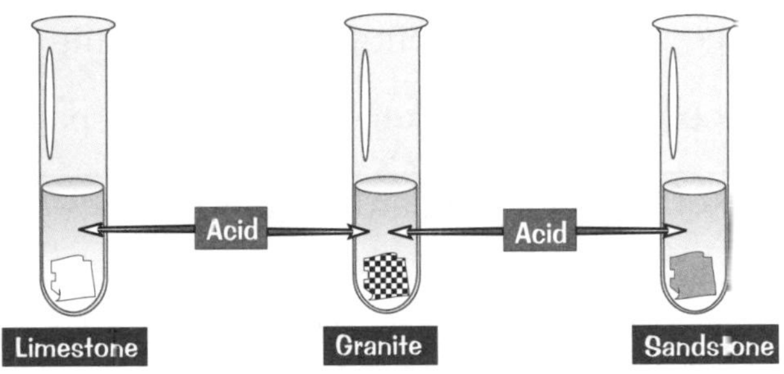

a) Fill in what you would expect their **observations** to be in their results table below.

Type of rock tested	Observations over 20 minutes
Granite	
Limestone	
Sandstone	

b) Paula and Kate's class visited their local church and found out that the church building and many gravestones were badly affected by acid rain.

i) What kind of building material was probably used here?

ii) What evidence of damage would the class have found showing that the church building and gravestones had been affected by acid rain?

Q2 Copy and complete the passage, choosing the missing words from the grey box.

REACTION ORGANISMS NEUTRALISE FISH
CORRODED BUILDING METAL

'Acid rain not only damages some types of .... stone but also has an effect on .... structures.

Metals are .... by acid rain in a chemical .... that weakens them.

Living .... may also be harmed by acid rain.
Acid rain damages trees and poisons .... in lakes.

Sometimes a base called lime is added to a lake to help .... its acidity.'

Monitoring Pollution

Q1 The local newspaper is running an investigation into a wave of illnesses among surfers in the town of Sunnysand-on-Sea.

There is a sewage pipe situated out to sea near to the beach.

Below are some of the quotes taken from the newspaper reporter's interviews.

"We are proud of the high standards of our beaches"

(Sunnysand-on-Sea tourist board)

"There has been an increase in the number of infections among beach users in the last 5 years"

(Sunnysand-on-Sea Health Authority)

"There is no significant risk to the general public from our sewage disposal operations"

(Water Authority)

"We know that there must be a link between seawater quality and the number of us getting ill"

(local surfer)

"You can see all sorts of toilet waste on the beach when I walk my dog, it's shocking"

(local resident)

a) Taking each quotation in turn as a piece of **evidence**, explain:

i) whether you think the evidence is **biased** or not

ii) whether the evidence is **useful** or not for the investigation

b) Do you think it is likely that the sea is polluted and affecting surfers?

Explain your answer using the evidence that you have.

c) What other evidence might you collect if you were the reporter? Explain your answer.

Q2 Jade (14) lives in a large busy town in Cumbria.

Jade's Grandad says air pollution in their town is much worse now than when he was Jade's age.

If you were to investigate Grandad's claim:

a) What **evidence** would you need to collect, and where from?

b) What sorts of evidence would be **reliable** and what would not?

c) What would be the **differences** between the types of evidence collected from the past and those from present day?

d) Explain the strengths and weaknesses of present day and past evidence.

I don't think I'd like to be a pollution monitor...

It's really important that we keep track of where pollution is getting worse, not just so we can say, "it wasn't like that in my day" — but so we can do something about it.

Global Warming

Q1 Copy and complete the paragraph using the words from the grey box: (you may use each word once, more than once or not at all.)

WARMING	COAL	NITROGEN	FOSSIL	ELEMENTS	CARBON	
pH	MILLIONS	OIL	ANIMALS	GREENHOUSE	ACIDITY	
DIOXIDE	GAS	PLANTS	BURNING	OXYGEN	GLOBAL	OXIDES

The fuels ...., ... and natural .... are called the .... fuels because they were formed .... of years ago from the remains of .... or .... People generally use these fuels by .... them. Burning the fuels releases .... which have been locked away in the fuels and reacts them with .... Two important pollutants produced are .... dioxide and sulphur .... Other .... of sulphur and oxides of .... are also released. These oxides increase the .... (lower the ....) of rain water. .... dioxide is called a .... gas and is believed to be a major cause of ....

Q2 Look at the graph and answer the questions which follow.

The graph shows how global temperatures have changed over the last 600 years.

The graph is made by combining information from many scientists using sources such as tree rings, historical records and direct measurements.

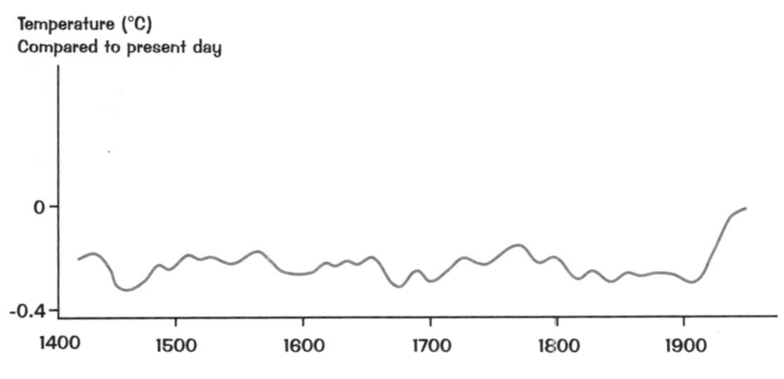

a) How can tree rings be used to measure temperature?

b) Why do we have to use data from tree rings?

c) How do scientists know what actual temperature relates to a particular pattern of growth?

d) What does the graph show about the changes in global temperature?

e) What makes this data reliable?

f) What is thought to have caused the temperature change?

g) Write down the sentences below which are thought to happen because of global warming.

A Weathering of buildings

B Drought in northern Africa

C The hole in the ozone layer

D Death of fish in Northern European lakes

E Reduction in the tiger population

F Melting of the Arctic ice cap

G Bleaching of coral reefs

Burning Fuels

Q1 Fuels are substances that give out energy when they burn. Write down the names of the **five** fuels in this list:

a) water
b) methane (natural gas)
c) petrol
d) electricity
e) diesel
f) dried cow dung
g) wood
h) wind

Q2 Copy and complete each of the labels on the diagram by choosing words from the grey box.

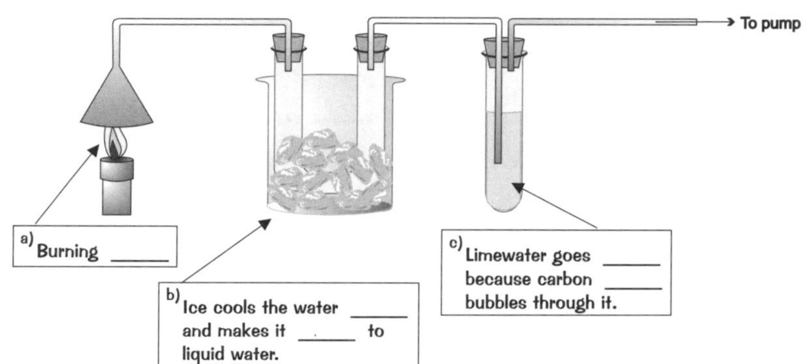

VAPOUR	METHANE
MILKY	CONDENSE
DIOXIDE	

Q3 Copy and complete the sentences below by choosing the correct word from each pair:

Fuels like methane gas and LPG (liquid propane gas) are hydrocarbons. They are made from **[hydrogen/hydroxide]** and **[chlorine/carbon]** only. When hydrocarbons burn in plenty of air, they react with **[nitrogen/oxygen]** to make carbon dioxide and **[water/nitrogen monoxide]**.

Q4 Copy and complete these equations to show the combustion products of petrol (a hydrocarbon):

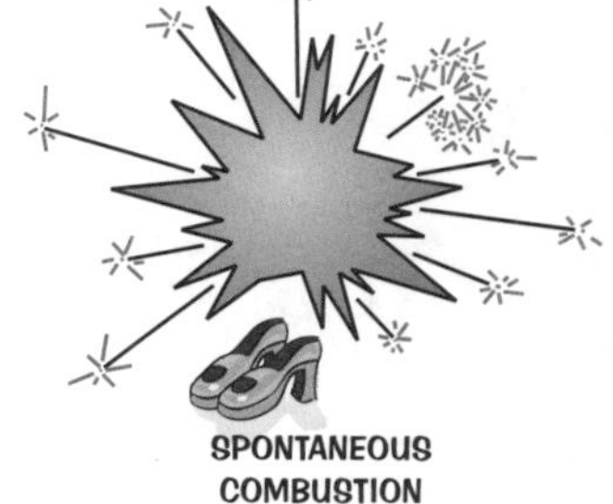

a) **Complete** combustion (when there is plenty of oxygen)

Petrol + oxygen ⟶ c.................. d.................. + water

b) **Incomplete** combustion (when there is less oxygen, for example in a car engine)

Petrol + oxygen ⟶ carbon dioxide + c.................. m..................
+ c.................. + water

Q5 We may be able to use hydrogen as a fuel in the future. Copy and complete the table by writing the statements from the grey box in the correct column:

We can produce it from water	It needs to be compressed for storage
It does not make carbon dioxide when it burns	A mixture of hydrogen and air explodes easily

Advantages of using hydrogen as a fuel	Disadvantages of using hydrogen as a fuel

Chemical Reactions as Energy Resources

Q1 Write down these metals in order of their reactivity. Put the most reactive metal first.

SILVER	MAGNESIUM	COPPER	IRON	ZINC	LEAD

Q2 Copy and complete the paragraph by choosing words from the grey box.

ELECTRICAL	ENERGY	SERIES	FURTHER	REACTIVITY

Many chemical reactions give out .... We use reactions involving metals to produce .... or heat energy. The amount of energy depends on the difference in .... of the metals. The .... apart the metals are in the Reactivity ...., the more energy they give out.

Q3 This cell produces electricity. The voltage is 1.1V.

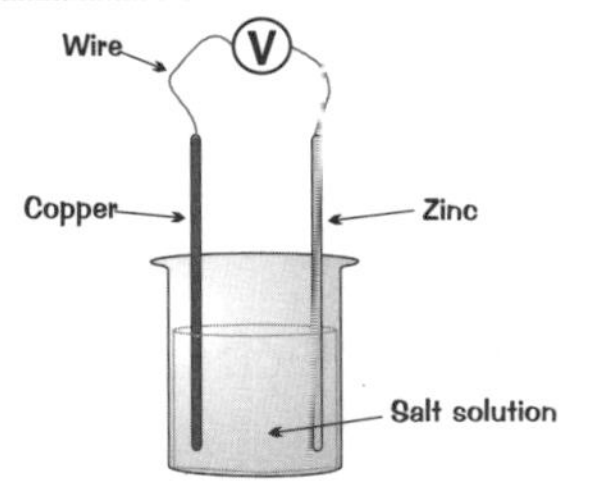

Copy and complete the sentences below, by choosing **one** word from each highlighted pair.

a) Joe made a cell using zinc and iron. The voltage was **[bigger/smaller]**.

b) Naomi made a cell using zinc and silver.
The cell produced **[more/less]** electrical energy than the original one.

c) Kezi made a cell using zinc and lead. The voltage was **[0.6V/2.0V]**.

d) One of the metals in car batteries is **[lead/silver]**.

Q4 If you put zinc powder into copper sulfate solution, the chemical reaction gives out heat energy so the temperature goes up. Use the metals in the grey box to answer the questions.

MAGNESIUM	ZINC	IRON	LEAD	COPPER	SILVER

Thermometer

Copper sulfate solution

Zinc powder

a) Choose **one** metal you could put in the solution to make the temperature go up more than it did with zinc.

b) Choose **two** metals that would make the temperature go up, but not as much as with zinc.

c) Choose **one** metal that would not react with the solution, and so would not make the temperature go up at all.

Running out of energy? Now you know how to make more...

Chemical reactions can be used to make energy. Fuel produces energy when it's burnt and lots of other reactions produce heat or electrical energy — pretty useful stuff.

Materials Made Through Chemical Reactions

Q1 Copy the table and write down each process in the correct column.

Chemical reactions that happen in living things	Chemical reactions that humans do to make useful substances

a) making plastic for mobile phones
b) making glucose in photosynthesis
c) cooking chips
d) respiration
e) breaking down starch to make glucose
f) making salmeterol for asthma inhalers
g) making potassium chlorate for match heads
h) making urine

Q2 From this list, write down five **chemical reactions** that humans use to produce useful energy.

a) burning coal to boil water and make steam to generate electricity
b) generating electricity from wind turbines
c) burning chicken litter to boil water and make steam to generate electricity
d) burning liquid propane gas (LPG) in bus engines
e) using a solar cooker to heat water
f) producing an electric current in nickel-cadmium rechargeable batteries
g) making liquid iron in the Thermit process to weld railway lines together
h) generating electricity from tidal power

Q3 A few years ago, scientists developed a medicine to treat high blood pressure. Write out the letters for the stages of development below in a sensible order.

(A) Scientists eventually made a similar chemical which lowered blood pressure but which did not break down in the stomach.

(B) Doctors found that more and more people in Europe and North America had high blood pressure. Pharmaceutical companies decided to develop a new drug to tackle the problem.

(C) They tested this chemical and found that it was no good as a medicine because its particles broke down in people's stomachs.

(D) Scientists found that the venom from a Brazilian snake makes its victims' blood pressure fall.

(E) The government gave the medicine a licence so that it could be sold.

(F) Doctors tested the medicine on human volunteers.

(G) They separated the chemicals in the venom to find the **one** chemical which makes blood pressure fall.

The Results of Chemical Reactions

Q1 Look at the diagram. Then copy and complete the writing using the words in the grey box.

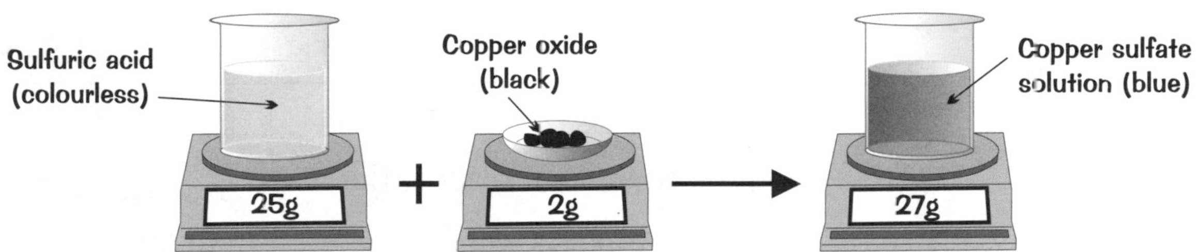

CONSERVED POWDER PRODUCT 27g SOLUTION

Carol mixed 25g of colourless sulfuric acid .... with 2g of black copper oxide .... This produced .... of blue copper sulfate solution. The total mass of the reactants (what she started with) was the same as the mass of the ....(what she made). Mass has been ....

Q2 Copy the diagrams and fill in the missing masses:

a) b)

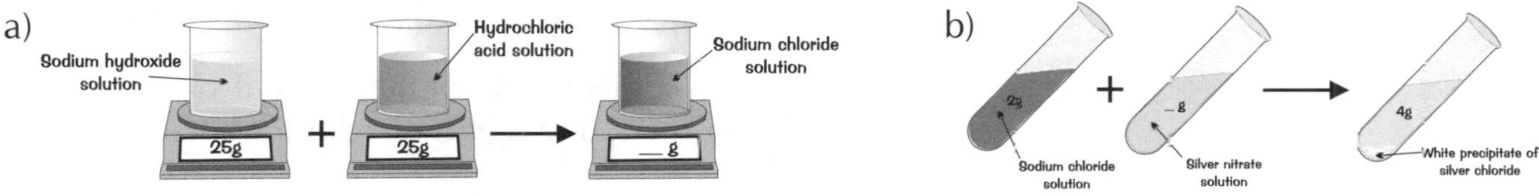

Q3 Write down the **three** true sentences about chemical reactions:

a) In chemical reactions, the atoms rearrange.

b) Some atoms disappear in chemical reactions.

c) There are the same numbers of atoms in the products as there are in the reactants.

d) Atoms are joined together differently in the reactants than they are in the products.

e) Atoms can change their mass in chemical reactions.

Q4 Copy the diagrams and draw one molecule in each box to complete the chemical equations.

a) c)

b) d)

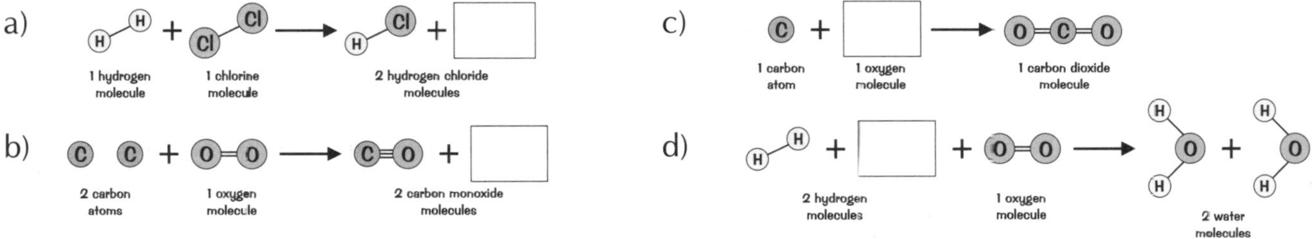

Masses and masses of chemical reactions...

With all these weights and equations it's all looking dangerously like maths. But just work through the questions and don't be put off. If you get any wrong, try try and try again — it's the only way.

The Results of Chemical Reactions

Q1 Copy and complete the sentences by choosing the words from the grey box to explain this experiment.

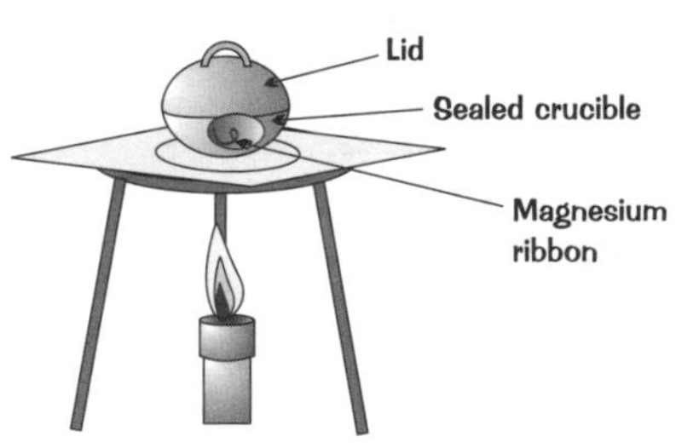

MAGNESIUM OXYGEN AIR INCREASED

Tilly burnt 1.0g of magnesium in .... and made 1.7g of magnesium oxide. The mass .... because magnesium joined with .... from the air.

.... + oxygen ⟶ magnesium oxide

Q2 Some other groups did the experiment in Q1. Here are their results:

Group	Mass of magnesium/g	Mass of magnesium oxide/g
A	0.12	0.20
B	0.21	0.35
C	0.60	1.00
D	0.75	1.25

The groups used all their results to plot this graph:

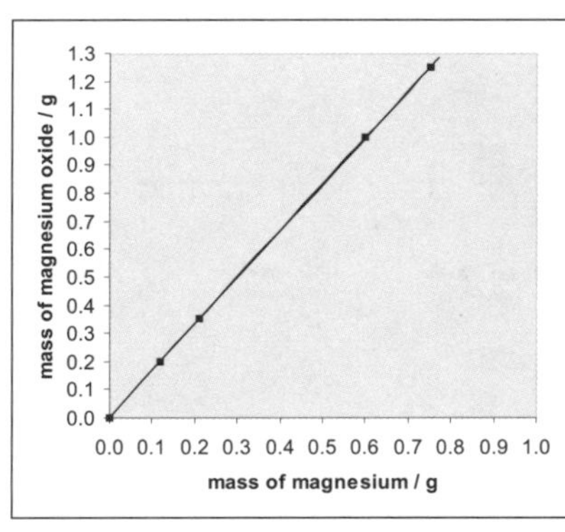

a) Group E started with 0.4g of magnesium. What mass of magnesium oxide should they make?

b) Group F made 0.8g of magnesium oxide. What mass of magnesium did they start with?

c) Group G made only 0.5g of magnesium oxide from 0.4g of magnesium. Give one possible reason why they made less magnesium oxide than expected.

Q3 Write down the first letter of each missing word to spell another word.

a) Hydrocarbons contain .... and carbon only.

b) When you burn hydrocarbons, ... make carbon dioxide and water.

c) .... is a hydrocarbon used as a fuel in lorries.

d) The .... between petrol and oxygen gives out lots of heat energy.

e) When a substance burns it joins with .... from the air.

f) Methane + oxygen ⟶ .... dioxide + water

g) Methane (natural gas) burns to make water and carbon dioxide which escape into the ....

h) .... + oxygen ⟶ rubidium oxide

i) When wax .... it makes carbon dioxide and water.

j) Hydrocarbons contain hydrogen and carbon ....

k) .... is a gas in the air which does not take part in burning reactions.

The Results of Chemical Reactions

Q1 Copy and complete the sentences using the words from the grey box.

In all chemical reactions:

PRODUCTS	CONSERVED
NEW	ARRANGEMENTS

a) .... materials are made.

b) The atoms join together in different ....

c) Mass is .... — the total mass of the .... is the same as that of the reactants.

Q2 If we see one or more of the changes below, there may have been a chemical reaction. Copy the statements and next to each write the letter of the most appropriate diagram.

In some chemical reactions,

a) we see a colour change

b) bubbles of gas are made

c) the temperature changes

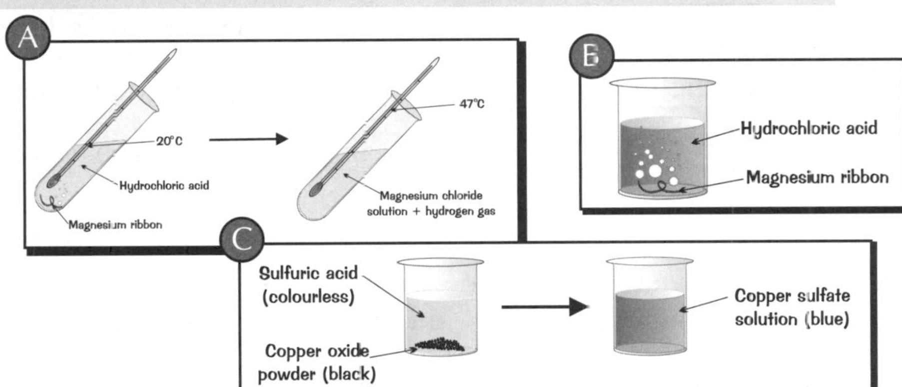

Q3 From the reactions in the box, write down:

a) One neutralisation reaction

b) Two reactions involving combination with oxygen

c) One displacement reaction

d) Two combustion (burning) reactions

Equation M: carbon + oxygen ⟶ carbon dioxide

Equation N: hydrochloric acid + sodium hydroxide ⟶ sodium chloride + water

Equation P: methane + oxygen ⟶ carbon dioxide + water

Equation Q: magnesium ribbon + copper sulfate solution ⟶ copper + magnesium sulfate solution

Q4 Write down a word equation for each description:

a) Arsenic burns in oxygen to make arsenic oxide

b) Nitric acid reacts with magnesium to make magnesium nitrate and hydrogen

Q5 Copy the word equations. Next to each one, write the correct symbol equation from the box.

a) sulphur + oxygen ⟶ sulphur dioxide

b) hydrochloric acid + sodium hydroxide ⟶ sodium chloride + water

c) magnesium + oxygen ⟶ magnesium oxide

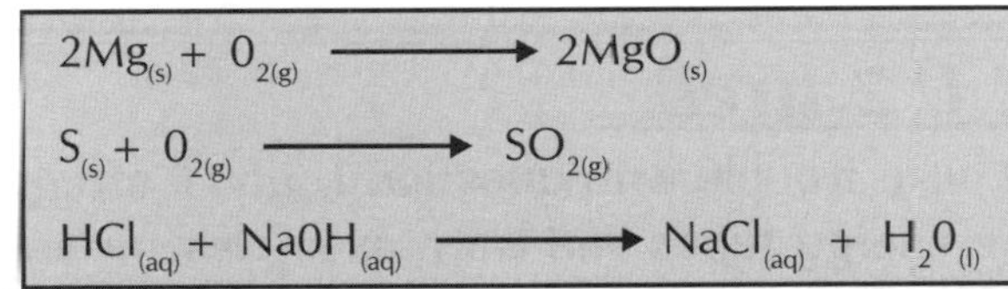

$2Mg_{(s)} + O_{2(g)} \longrightarrow 2MgO_{(s)}$

$S_{(s)} + O_{2(g)} \longrightarrow SO_{2(g)}$

$HCl_{(aq)} + NaOH_{(aq)} \longrightarrow NaCl_{(aq)} + H_2O_{(l)}$

Uses of Energy

Q1 Match these energy types to their descriptions. The first one has been done for you.

Energy type	Description
Nuclear →	The energy released by splitting atoms.
Electrical	The energy that you need in a catapult.
Light	The kind of energy carried by charges going around a circuit.
Heat or Thermal	Energy that you give to something when you lift it into the air.
Kinetic	A noisy class is a good source of this.
Chemical	This kind of energy helps you to see where you're going.
Sound	A moving train has a lot of this energy.
Elastic Potential	The energy in food, fuels and inside batteries.
Gravitational Potential	Hot objects have plenty of this kind of energy.

Q2 These devices all change electrical energy into other forms. What is the most useful kind of energy that each one makes?

a) Loudspeaker b) Toaster

c) Battery charger d) Smoke detector

e) Drill f) Computer screen

g) Alarm clock

Q3 Name a common device, machine or type of power station that can make electrical energy from these types of energy.

a) Sound b) Chemical c) Light

d) Gravitational Potential e) Elastic Potential f) Kinetic

Q4 All these machines have an energy store inside them. What kind of energy is stored and how is it stored?

a) Car b) Grandfather clock c) Walkman

d) Wind up toy e) You f) Match

Got N R G 4 work — or R U 2 tired...

Question 1 is dead important. If you have trouble with question 1, you'll struggle with a lot of other questions. Memorise all nine energy types and learn examples for each of them.

Energy Transfer — Circuits

Q1 Match each word on the left to the correct explanation on the right.

Circuit	A dried up grape that you find in a cake.
Closed	The end of a cell or battery.
Open	A flow of electrical charges around a circuit.
Copper	A device for measuring current or voltage.
Insulator	A black and white line drawing that represents a real component.
Battery	A good conductor used inside wires.
Metre	Two or more cells joined end to end.
Current	The switch contacts have a gap between them so the circuit is off.
Currant	A complete conducting path which allows something electrical to work.
Symbol	The metric unit of length.
Meter	Something which won't conduct electricity.
Terminal	The switch contacts are shut together so that a current can flow.

Q2 Which of these statements are true?

A Current is used up as it goes around the circuit.
B Current flows from the positive to the negative end of the cell.
C Electricity is a form of energy.
D The current in a series circuit is the same at all points.
E The voltage in a series circuit is the same at all points.
F The total of the voltage drop around a series circuit, equals the voltage of the battery.

Q3 Copy out and complete the passage using: **ammeter, voltmeter, series, parallel, damaged.**

Voltage is measured with a .... which must be connected in ....

Current is measured with an .... which always goes into a circuit in ....

It is very difficult to damage a .... in a circuit but if it's connected wrongly the circuit won't work properly. If you are trying to measure current and get it wrong by connecting an .... in .... then it could get ....

Q4 Four students are trying to find the voltage and current for lamp A in their circuits.

a) Which student(s) listened to their teacher and connected their circuit(s) up correctly?

b) Draw correct circuits for the ones that are wrong.

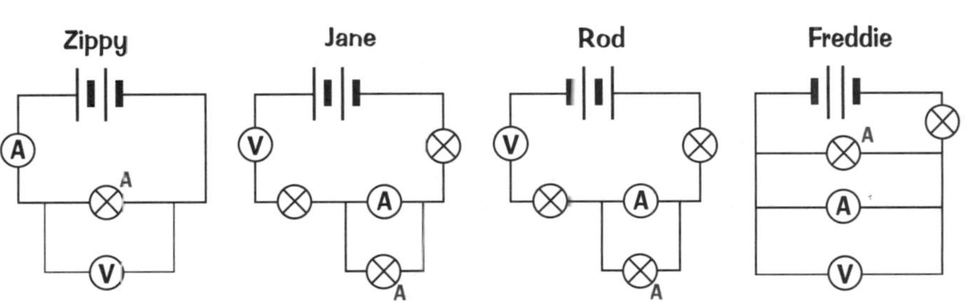

Energy Transfer — Circuits

Q1 Teachers and examiners use lots of different ideas to explain current and voltage.

For the three "models" identify:

a) The part of the model that is meant to be the current.

b) The part of the model that acts like a battery.

c) The part of the model that acts like a voltage drop, or place where energy is lost.

d) A reason why this model is confusing compared with real electricity.

Model 1:
A pump lifts water uphill to a lake. The water flows downhill through a water wheel. The water wheel drives a model water mill. After the water wheel the water is pumped back up the hill.

Model 2:
A chair lift carries skiers up a long hill. The skiers then ski back down the mountain. The skiers control their speed by carving up great heaps of snow or crashing into things. The skiers finally make it back to the bottom of the lift and then go up it again.

Model 3
Ten people are playing Monopoly. Each time they pass go they are given £200. As they carry on around the board they use the money up. Finally they get back to go and get more money.

Q2 Copy out the sentences below, choosing the correct words where there's a choice.

a) A dry cell contains [chemicals / mechanisms] which are [not used up / gradually used up] as the cell supplies electrical energy.

b) A simple dry cell uses a graphite rod inside a [zinc and steel / lithium or mercury] case but it isn't very powerful.

c) Modern high power cells use metals like [zinc and steel / lithium and mercury].

d) These metals are very [poisonous / sharp] so you shouldn't mess about with them.

e) A cell can be made by sticking pieces of [wood / metal] into a [rock / lemon].

f) The citric acid in the lemon dissolves the [skin / metal] and produces a [chemical / voltage].

Q3 Give a reason for each of these safety rules.

a) Always try to recycle batteries or dispose of them properly.

b) Never fish under electricity pylons.

c) Don't go into electrical substations.

d) Never take the back off a television set, even if the power is off.

e) Don't play on railway lines.

f) Never stick anything other than a proper plug into a power socket.

The Cost of Electricity

Q1 Use the words, numbers or units below to complete these sentences.

kWh, energy, kilowatt, voltage, current, power, kilo, watts, hour(s), 200, 230, 250, time

a) In Britain the mains electricity supply is at .... volts.

b) The unit used on electricity bills is the ....

c) The power rating of an appliance is measured in ....

d) The .... used by an appliance depends on its .... in kilowatts and the .... in .... that it is on for.

e) One .... is the amount of electrical energy used by an appliance with a .... of one .... used for a time of one ....

f) The power of an appliance depends on both the .... in amps and the .... in volts.

Q2 Match the power ratings to the appliances and put them in order of power demand.

100 W, 800 W, 15000 W, 300 W, 1200 W, 20 W

Q3 A student's room has a TV (250 W), heater (1000 W) and lamp (100 W). Electricity costs 10p per unit. So the heater would cost 10p to run for one hour. How much does it cost to run:

a) The lamp for 20 hours?

b) The TV for 12 hours?

c) The lamp for 5 hours?

d) The heater and TV for 4 hours?

e) The light and TV for 24 hours?

f) All three for 2 hours?

Q4 Explain the following giving a scientific reason where possible:

a) Electricity bills are bigger in winter rather than summer.

b) Leaving a TV on all night is worse than leaving a lamp on.

c) A computer uses less energy than a fan heater if they are on for the same length of time.

d) One kilowatt of sound is deafening but a one kilowatt fire hardly warms a big room up.

e) Leaving appliances on standby costs you money and is bad for the environment.

Shocking — the cost of electricity today... ***(there should be a bad joke toll on that one)***

Electricity cost sums are simple maths, but make sure you check them. Learn the voltage of the British supply and learn power ratings by ordering a list of appliances by their power demands.

Making Electricity

Q1 My computer has garbled up some words. Correct the words and copy the passage.

Electricity is **green date** in a **woper o sat nit**. A **me rants orrf** converts it to a very high **gave lot** for transmission over the **woper lon spy**. This **gave lot** is far too high to be safe in your house so a **me rants orrf** in a **bus is on tat** drops the **gave lot** down to 230 V.

This then enters your house at the **scumer no u nit** where the **treem** measures the amount of energy that your house uses.

Q2 Which of these statements are true and which are false?

a) Burning fossil fuels is one of the main causes of global warming.

b) Global warming is caused by there being too many greenhouses.

c) CFCs (chlorofluorocarbons) are nothing to do with global warming.

d) Nuclear waste is harmless if left alone for ten years.

e) Vehicle exhausts contribute to acid rain.

f) Coal reserves will run out before natural gas.

g) Cars cannot run on electrical energy.

h) Solar panels can work on cloudy days.

The true cause of global warming...

Q3 The good points and bad points are all mixed up in this table.
Copy out the table and put the good points and bad points in the correct boxes.

Type of Power Station	Good Points	Bad Points
Wind Turbine	Causes acid rain and global warming.	Needs a lot of land and good management to be renewable.
Nuclear	The fuel could run out in less than 50 years.	Provides habitat for birds and insects.
Coal Burning	Has been linked to earthquakes. Displaces poor people from their farmland.	Could have very bad effects on wading birds.
Gas Burning	Plenty of fuel still available.	A large amount of energy comes from a small quantity of fuel.
Tidal	No fuel burnt so no harmful emissions.	No fuel burnt so no pollution.
Hydro-electric Power	Able to produce power twice every day regardless of the weather.	The cleanest of the fossil fuels.
Biomass	Some people think that they are noisy and ugly.	The waste produced is dangerous for thousands of years.

Reducing Energy Waste

Q1 These six sentences are all about how energy is wasted when electricity is made from coal. Explain how energy is wasted at each of these stages.

a) Coal is extracted from deep underground.

b) It needs to be transported to the power station.

c) The coal needs to be crushed before it is burned.

d) Energy is lost in the steam from the cooling towers.

e) The electricity needs to be transmitted long distances over the national grid.

f) Electricity is used by lots of electrical appliances in your house.

Q2 How good are electric cars for the environment? The sentences below describe aspects of the electric car where energy is wasted. Describe how the energy is wasted in each case.

a) The metal and plastic parts of the car need to be made and shaped.

b) The components are transported all over the world.

c) The car uses electricity.

d) Air resistance affects the car as it's driven.

Q3 Explain why all these steps that you could take are good for the environment. Give at least two reasons for each one.

a) You should replace old fashioned metal filament lamps with low energy ones.

b) You should walk to school rather than go in a car.

c) If you can't walk to school then you should use a bus or train.

d) You should use buses or trains rather than aeroplanes to go on holiday.

e) You should try to send emails rather than send loads of paper all over the planet.

f) Turn the monitor on your computer off rather than run a screen saver all day if you're not using the beast.

g) Recycle all the glass, metal and paper that you use.

h) Drink tap water rather than stuff that comes in plastic bottles.

Write smaller — it saves energy...

Energy is only useful when it's converted from one form to another and energy conversion always involves some wastage. Learn the ways energy is wasted and how it can be used more efficiently.

Gravity, Mass and Weight

Q1 Copy and complete this paragraph.

The force of gravity on you is called your [mass / weight]. This force pulls you towards the [centre / surface] of the Earth. If you were on the Moon or a planet which is [smaller / bigger] than Earth your [weight / mass] would be less but your [weight / mass] would stay the same.

Weight is calculated from [distance / mass] x [gravitational field / mass] strength.

On Earth the [gravitational field / mass] strength is about [ten / one] N/kg.

Q2 This rocket will only get off the ground if weight and thrust are right.

a) Sketch the rocket, draw on the correct arrows (choosing from the options given) and label them 'Thrust' and 'Weight'.

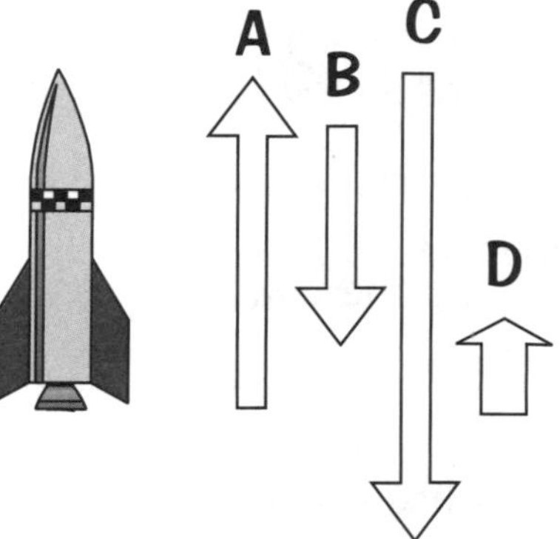

b) Write TRUE or FALSE for these sentences.

i) The rocket will escape from gravity once it is outside the atmosphere.

ii) The rocket's mass gets less as it rises.

iii) The rocket rises at constant speed.

iv) The force of gravity on the rocket gets less as it rises.

v) The rocket's weight gets less as it rises.

Q3 Copy and complete this table to work out the weight of different things on different planets.

OBJECT	PLANET	GRAVITATIONAL FIELD STRENGTH (N/kg)	WEIGHT (N)
Peter (mass = 60 kg)	Mercury	3.9	
1.5 kg bag of flour	Jupiter	25.0	
1000 kg car	Uranus	12.0	
100 g apple	Pluto	0.6	

Q4 In the word search find the names of...

...the first man in space.

...the first woman in space.

...the first man on the Moon.

...the first British person in space.

...the first dog in space.

V	X	G	N	A	M	R	A	H	S
A	C	A	V	V	O	N	O	E	L
N	A	G	O	I	K	T	E	R	E
I	N	A	L	E	X	E	I	H	S
T	E	R	E	S	H	K	O	V	A
N	I	I	X	E	I	V	U	R	I
E	L	N	R	T	L	R	I	E	N
L	T	N	E	L	E	H	U	S	T
A	K	I	A	L	N	G	O	Y	R
V	G	N	O	R	T	S	M	R	A

Gravity, Mass and Weight

Q1 Everybody has seen pictures of how astronauts move on the Moon (find out if you haven't). Make one sentence out of some of the jumbled bits below to explain the way they move.

The astronauts have less weight...

The astronauts have less mass...

...because the Moon's gravity is weaker than Earth's.

...because they are a long way from the Earth.

Q2 The table below shows how the strength of the gravitational force on each kilogram (gravitational field strength) changes on a journey to the Moon.

a) Write a sentence to explain why the numbers in the last column get smaller to start with.

DISTANCE FROM EARTH (km)	DISTANCE FROM MOON (km)	GRAVITATIONAL FIELD STRENGTH (N/kg)
0	377,600	9.814
38,400	345,600	0.272
76,800	307,200	0.068
115,200	268,800	0.030
153,600	230,400	0.017
192,000	192,000	0.011
230,400	153,600	0.007
268,800	115,200	0.005
307,200	76,800	0.002
345,600	38,400	0.000
382,300	0	1.713

b) The sentences below are about when the Gravitational Field Strength is '0'. Write TRUE or FALSE for each one.

i) The rocket has reached the end of Earth's gravity.

ii) The forces on it are balanced.

iii) It is half way between the Earth and the Moon.

iv) The Moon's force on it is the same size as the Earth's.

c) One of the astronauts' mass is 50kg. Use the table to calculate her weight when she is:

i) On Earth.

ii) 192000km from Earth.

iii) 345600km from Earth.

iv) At the Moon.

d) Apart from its size, write down what would be different about the force at the Moon compared to the force at the Earth.

THIS GRAVITY IS GETTING ME DOWN...

If you learn nothing else from these two pages make sure you learn this: MASS is the amount of matter something contains, WEIGHT is the affect of gravity on mass. NOW LEARN IT GOOD.

The Solar System

Q1 The picture below shows an ancient idea of what the Solar System is like.

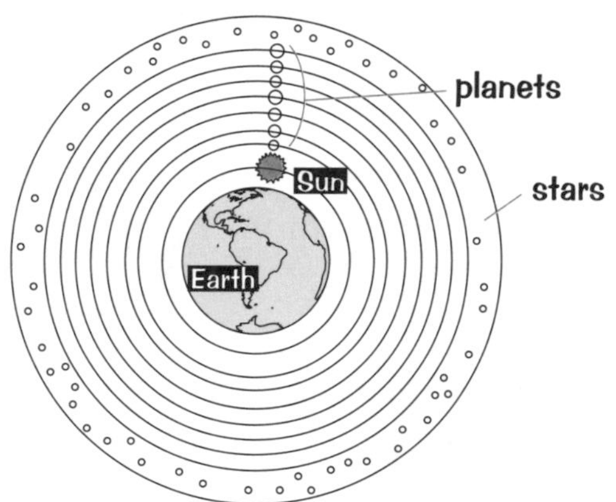

a) Write down three differences between this model and our modern picture of the Solar System.

b) The sort of picture shown above is called a GEOCENTRIC model. Write down a sentence to explain what is meant by the word GEOCENTRIC.

c) What is the name (even longer than 'geocentric'!) used for our modern model of the Solar System?

Q2 The phrases below are about what the models of the Solar System can do.

- Explains the daily motion of the Sun and Moon.
- Explains seasons.
- Fits in with the rules of gravity.
- Can be used to predict eclipses.
- Explains in a simple way why the planets seem to go backwards sometimes.

a) Write down which are true of a GEOCENTRIC system.

b) Write down which are true of a HELIOCENTRIC system.

Q3 The list below is of a few very important stages in the history of astronomy. Write down each stage and the name of the person who did it from this list.

- Predicted a solar eclipse in 585BC.
- Proposed an early heliocentric theory.
- Published a book outlining the heliocentric theory.
- Provided very accurate observations.
- Used ellipses for the planets' orbits which fitted perfectly with the observations.
- Used a telescope and found Jupiter's moons, and mountains on our Moon.
- Produced a theory of gravity which explained why the planets move in ellipses.

Johannes Kepler
Aristarchus of Samos
Tycho Brahe
Nicolaus Copernicus
Isaac Newton
Galileo Galilei
Thales of Miletus

Planetary Orbits

Q1 This is a diagram of a planet moving round the Sun.

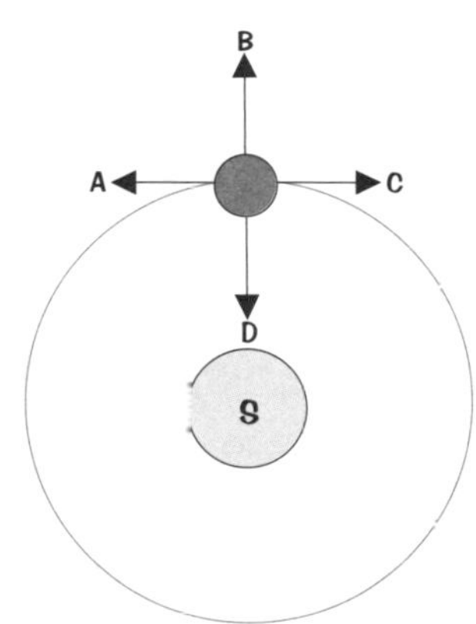

Write down the letter of the arrow which shows...

a) the direction of the gravitational force on this planet.

b) the general direction it would move if the force were suddenly switched off.

Q2 Copy and complete this paragraph.

The M................ is the Earth's n................ satellite. It orbits once every t................ days. It is kept in orbit due to Earth' g................ force. The Moon feels a stronger force from the E................ than from the Sun because it is much c................ to the E.................. .

Q3 This table gives information about planetary orbits round the Sun.

Name	Mercury	Venus	Earth	Mars	Jupiter	Saturn
Average distance from the sun (millions km)	58	108	150	228	778	1427
Orbit time (years)	0.24	0.62	1	1.88	11.87	29.53
Average speed (?)						

a) Draw a bar chart to show the average distance from the Sun of the planets in the table.

b) You can get an average **speed** for each planet by using the formula below.

$$\text{Average Speed} = \frac{\text{Average distance from the Sun} \times 6.28}{\text{Orbit time}}$$

Copy and complete the table, not forgetting to write what the speed would be measured in.

c) Write down what happens to the speed of the planets as you go further from the Sun.

d) What causes this change?

How quick's the Earth going! — open the window, I'm gonna chuck...

You might think I'm being boring here, but I think the story of how humans came to understand the universe is flippin' interesting — Copernicus is my favourite. Even if you're just thinking "who is this dullard", learning about the people WILL lodge the facts firmly in your skull. Just do it.

Satellites

Q1 Write TRUE or FALSE for each of these statements about satellites.

a) The word satellite means spacecraft.

b) The International Space Station is a satellite.

c) Galileo saw satellites with his telescope.

d) 'Sputnik' was a satellite.

e) The 'Voyager' spacecraft (now far beyond Pluto) is a satellite.

f) Once in the correct orbit, satellites do not need engines to keep them going round.

g) All artificial satellites stay above a fixed point on Earth all the time.

h) TV satellites are all at the same height above the Earth.

i) The orbit for a TV satellite is called a Polar orbit.

By Jove, I see a satellite

Q2 Copy and complete this paragraph using the words from the grey box below.
You can use each word ONCE, MORE THAN ONCE or NOT AT ALL.

Earth	communication	height	longitude	once	24	12
twice	polar	all	geostationary	part	fixed	military	TV

Some artificial satellites need to stay above a .... point on the Earth's surface. Satellites which do this include .... and .... satellites. This means that they must orbit the Earth .... every .... hours. To make this happen they all have to be at the same .... This type of orbit is called .... The other main type of orbit is a .... orbit. This allows a satellite to scan .... of the surface of the .... observation satellites use this sort of orbit.

Q3
a) What 'A' is always caused between objects due to gravity?
b) What 'C' is the part of the Earth that gravity pulls you towards?
c) What 'N' is the unit of force?
d) What 'W' is the name for the force of gravity on you?
e) What 'M' is not affected by where you are?
f) What 'T' is the force a rocket needs to escape from Earth?
g) What 'H' is a satellite that has made a major contribution to astronomy?
h) What 'M' was home to the first British astronaut in space?
i) What 'G' used a telescope to change the world?

Speed, Distance and Time

Q1 Mandeep and Alison cycle to school. Mandeep takes 15 minutes. Alison takes 20 minutes.

a) Write down what else you need to know to work out who cycles faster.

b) They decide to measure their speed in the playground.

i) Write down what has to be kept the same for both of them.

ii) Write down what they need to measure.

iii) Write down the name of a suitable measuring instrument they could use.

c) Alison notices that she is getting faster as she cycles.
Write down the scientific word for getting faster.

Q2 Courtney, Michael and Rajiv have a race round the running track. Rajiv wins, Michael is second and Courtney third. Write down TRUE or FALSE for each of these statements.

a) Rajiv will have taken the longest time.

b) Courtney has the lowest average speed.

c) They must run the same distance to make it fair.

Q3 Put these units into three lists — one for DISTANCE, one for SPEED, one for TIME.

m/s s cm km/h km h cm/s m mm/s mm

Q4 Copy and complete this EQUATION: SPEED = ________ ÷ ________

Q5 Copy out this table and fill in the speeds.

Distance (m)	Time (s)	Speed (m/s)
10	5	
100	4	
2	10	

Q6 The fastest race horse ever recorded ran 804 m in 20.8 s, work out and write down his speed in m/s.

Q7 Archie, the world's fastest snail, covered 33 cm in 140 s in 1995. Work out his speed in cm/s and write down your answer.

Distance over time — 2 mph on Virgin*, if you're lucky...

Speed equals distance over time. Speed equals distance over time. Speed equals distance over time. Speed equals distance over time. Repeat after me: "Speed equals distance over time..."

* Only joking. Virgin trains are lovely.

Speed, Distance and Time

Q1 Roisin is on a long car journey with her mum. Her mum tells her 'We've been managing 40 mph overall'. 'No,' says Roisin 'it's often been less than that!'

a) Write down how Roisin knows that the speed has been less than 40 mph.

b) Her mother has done a quick calculation to come up with 40 mph. Write down what she has done.

c) One of them is talking about 'average speed', one of them is talking about 'speed at a point'. Write down who is talking about which.

Q2 In the lab Sarah and Afreka are rolling a car down a long ramp and measuring its speed at different points. They are using complicated equipment called a light gate and data logger.

a) Why they can't use a stop clock for this?

b) What you would expect to happen to the car's speed as it goes down the ramp?

c) What you would expect to happen if they made the ramp steeper?

Q3 For each of these statements write down TRUE or FALSE.

a) If I run to school in 5 minutes I am going twice as fast as my brother who walks the same way in 10 minutes.

b) Peter drives a 6 km journey in 10 minutes. He is going the same speed as Kevin who drives a 30 km journey in one hour.

c) The average speed for the 200 m world record is less than for the 100 m world record. The world 100 m record time is 9.79 s, the world 200 m record time is 19.32 s.

d) If I run at a constant speed between two marks, my 'average speed' and my 'speed at a point' will be the same.

Q4 Copy and complete this table, filling in either the SPEED, DISTANCE or the TIME **and** the missing UNIT.

Distance	Time	Speed
5 metres	2 seconds	
	4 hours	50 km/h
1 km		10 m/s

Rolling cars down a ramp — you ain't seen me, right...

Formula triangles — they'rrre grrreat. Learn how to use them *now*. Cover up the thing you're trying to find and whatever's left tells you how to find it. It really is that simple.

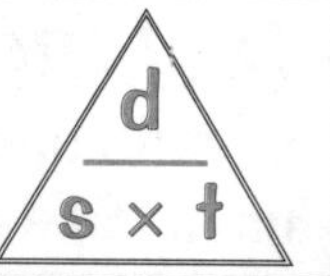

Forces and Speed

Q1 Write down the name of the following:

a) A force that always slows things down.

b) The force that makes a boat float.

c) The force that makes us have weight.

d) The force that sends a rocket into space.

Q2 Write down the names of the forces labelled w, x, y or z in these pictures.

a)

b)

c)

d)

Q3 Copy and complete each of these sentences choosing words from the grey box.
You can use any word ONCE, MORE THAN ONCE or NOT AT ALL.

LIGHT	HEAVY	STRONG	WEAK	ACCELERATION	FORCE	MASS

a) Sprinters need to be .... to provide more .... for acceleration.

b) Sprinters need to be .... as a small .... will accelerate more quickly.

c) A .... car will need more braking .... to stop it.

d) Racing cars are kept as light as possible to increase their ....

Q4 For the events below write down whether the forces are BALANCED or UNBALANCED.

a) A cyclist starting off.

b) A car slowing down.

c) A ski jumper accelerating down the slope.

d) A marathon runner going at a steady speed along a straight road.

e) (Difficult) A 200m runner 'running the bend' at a steady speed.

Speed and Friction

Q1 Copy and complete each of these sentences choosing words from the grey box. You can use any word ONCE, MORE THAN ONCE or NOT AT ALL.

REDUCE	FORCE	WATER	AIR	FRICTIONAL
RESISTANCE	WEIGHT	STREAMLINED		

a) When you walk or run you need a force to balance the frictional ....

b) The fictional force you feel when you move through air is called air ....

c) When you move through .... you will feel water resistance against you.

d) Dolphins have a .... shape to reduce .... resistance.

e) Streamlining is done to .... the .... forces.

Q2 Write down the names of three sports where streamlining is very important.

Q3 For each of these sentences write down whether it is TRUE or FALSE.

a) Frictional forces are highest on a car when it is just starting off.

b) A car uses more fuel to travel along at a 60 mph than at 40 mph.

c) The frictional forces on a racing cyclist increase as she accelerates.

d) When a speed boat reaches its top speed there is no frictional force on it.

Q4 Copy and complete this paragraph choosing words from the grey box. You can use any word ONCE, MORE THAN ONCE or NOT AT ALL.

Shazia is in the car with her Dad and it's raining. She notices that he needs the windscreen wipers on .... when the car is moving than when it is standing .... 'That's just like air .... ,' she says, 'its caused by more air .... hitting you when you move through the air. The .... you go the more particles hit you and the .... air resistance there is.

SLOWER	LESS	CURRENT	FASTER	HEAT	PRESSURE
RESISTANCE	PARTICLES	STILL	MORE		

Fictional forces — Stormtroopers, Klingons and the Nazgûl...*

Tricky to get your head round, this. If you're travelling at a constant speed, you're not accelerating. True, you have to keep your foot on the pedal to keep moving, but that's just to balance out the friction forces from the air and the road. Don't get caught out because it's called an "accelerator".

* Today's gag was brought to you by a selection of three of our finest editors.

Parachutes

Q1 Write down the sentences below which are TRUE about parachutists.

A: The force pulling them down is the force of gravity (weight).

B: The force which pushes upwards is mostly upthrust.

C: Weight decreases as they fall.

D: They reach a steady speed after a while.

E: Opening the parachute increases air resistance.

Q2 The four diagrams below show the parachutist at different times during her fall. Write down the correct description of her movement from the list below. You can use each description ONCE, MORE THAN ONCE or NOT AT ALL.

STEADY SPEED ACCELERATING SLOWING DOWN

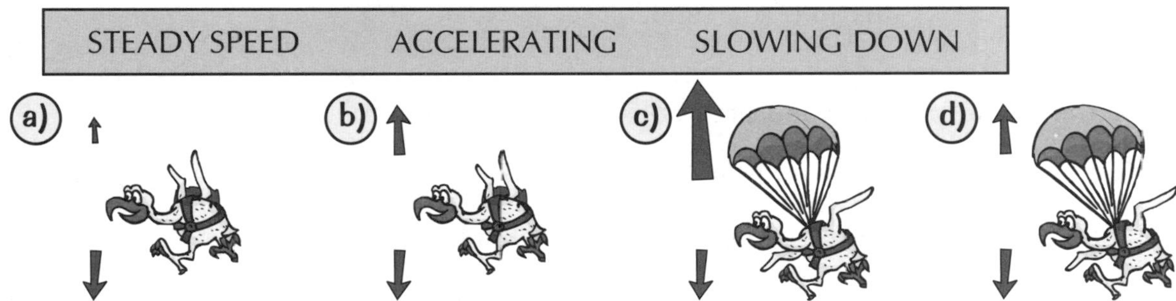

Q3 Copy the phrases below, but in the correct order, to tell the story of Sarah's parachute jump from leaving the plane to landing (safely) on the ground

She jumps out of the plane.
She moves at a constant speed.
She accelerates.
This force stays the same.
This is due to gravity pulling her down.
This slows her down.
This reduces the air resistance.
This force increases as she gets faster.
This increases the air resistance.
She moves at a slower constant speed.
She opens her parachute.
Air resistance pushes upwards on her.
Eventually the forces are balanced.
She lands.

Q4 The speed-time graph below is correct for Sarah's jump. Write down **what** is happening to her speed at points A, B, C and D and **why**.

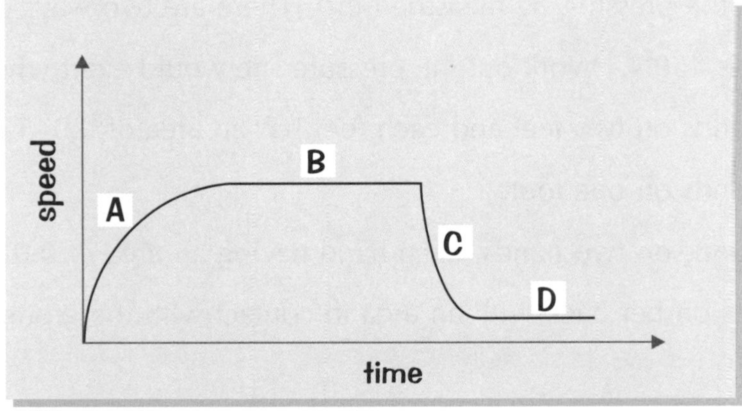

Pressure

Q1 Copy and complete the following sentences using the words **area** and **pressure**.

a) The .... produced by a force depends on the .... over which the force acts.

b) An ordinary car has a small .... in contact with the ground. This means that it exerts a large .... and so would sink in soft ground.

c) A bulldozer or tractor has a large .... in contact with the ground. This means that it exerts a small .... and so does not sink in soft ground.

d) A horse has a small .... in contact with the ground. This means that it exerts a large .... and so would sink into soft sand.

e) A camel has a large .... in contact with the ground. This means that it exerts a small .... and so would not sink into soft sand.

Q2 Using the words **pressure** and **area** correctly, explain the following.

a) Shark teeth sink easily into flesh.

b) A person wearing snow shoes would not sink into soft snow.

c) A lady in stiletto heeled shoes would damage a wooden floor but an elephant would not.

d) An Indian fakir can lie on a bed of nails without injuring himself.

Q3 A company is thinking of marketing a new safety drawing pin which has a large blunt end instead of a small sharp point. Use your ideas about area and pressure to explain why this would not be a good idea.

Q4 A pupil measures her weight in newtons using some bathroom scales. She then measures the area she has in contact with the ground in some different situations.

a) Write down the equation she would need to know to help her work out the pressure she exerts when she knows her weight(force) and her area.

b) When the weight is measured in newtons and the area in m^2, what would the pressure be measured in? [There are two ways of writing this down].

c) Her weight is 450N. Work out the pressure she would exert when:

i) She stands on two feet and each foot has an area of 0.045 m^2.

ii) She stands on one foot.

iii) She stands on two hands, each hand having an area of 0.015 m^2.

iv) She lies on her back with an area in contact with the ground of 0.5 m^2.

Pneumatics and Hydraulics

Q1 A girl pumps up her bicycle tyres using a bicycle pump.
Copy and complete the following sentences chosing the correct word from each pair.

a) In ordinary air there are **[large/small]** spaces between the molecules of the air.

b) The air molecules exert a pressure on a surface because they are moving very **[slowly/rapidly]** and colliding with the surface.

c) Each time the girl pushes the pump, **[more/less]** air is pumped into the tyre.

d) The molecules of the air inside the tyre are getting **[further apart/closer together]**.

e) The pressure of the air in the tyre is **[increasing/decreasing]**.

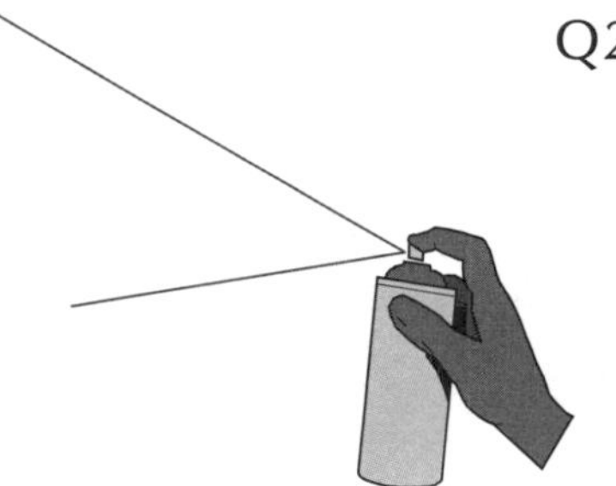

Q2 An aerosol can of air freshener releases tiny drops of liquid into the air when the release valve is pressed.

a) Describe in a sentence what is present in the aerosol as well as the liquid air freshener.

b) Explain briefly how this helps the liquid air freshener to be propelled into the room.

c) Write a sentence to explain why it is dangerous to puncture the can or put it on a fire.

Q3 Steam used to be used to drive railway engines. Copy and complete the following sentences using the correct word each time.

a) In a steam engine, burning coal or wood is used to **[heat/cool]** water.

b) The water turns to steam, which has a much **[smaller/larger]** volume than water.

c) As more water is heated, the pressure of the steam **[increases/decreases]**.

d) When the high pressure steam **[expands/contracts]** in a cylinder, it drives a piston along the cylinder, which makes the engine move.

All these new-matics to learn — it's a lot of pressure...

The main thing to remember is the equation: *pressure = force ÷ area.*
If you remember that equation and understand it then you can't go wrong.

Pneumatics and Hydraulics

Q1 A teacher asks a group of pupils to investigate whether air and water can be squashed. She gives them a plastic syringe and a beaker of water.

a) A pupil puts his finger over the end of the syringe and pushes on the plunger.

i) What happens to the volume of the air in the syringe?

ii) What does the pupil feel on his finger?

iii) Has the amount of air in the syringe changed?

iv) What has changed in the air apart from its volume?

v) What has happened to the distance apart of the molecules in the air?

vi) How could the pupil make the pressure of the air in the syringe less than normal?

b) The pupil then fills the syringe with water.
He puts his finger over the end of the syringe and pushes the plunger again.

i) What happens to the volume of the water in the syringe?

ii) What does the pupil feel on his finger?

iii) How far apart are the molecules of water in the syringe compared to the distance apart of the air molecules?

iv) The pupil's finger accidentally slips off the end of the syringe while the plunger is still being pushed hard. What happens to the water in the syringe?

Q2 A hydraulic press is used to make the effect of a force bigger.
The diagram shows a simple hydraulic press.

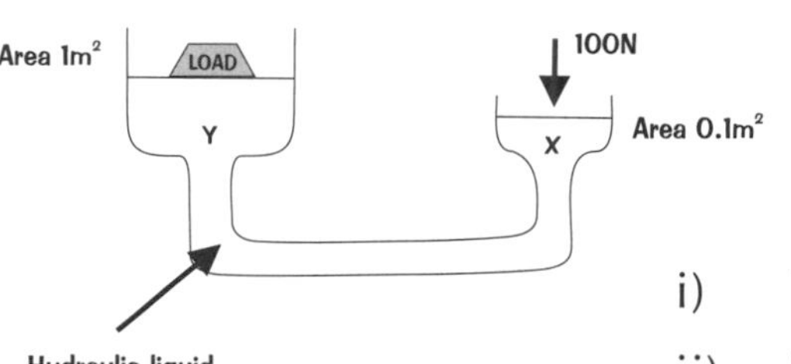

a) A force of 100N pushes down on the reservoir of a hydraulic press which has an area of $0.1m^2$.
This lifts a load on the other reservoir of the press, which has an area of $1m^2$.

i) What is the pressure in the liquid at point X?

ii) What is the pressure in the liquid at point Y?

iii) The force of 100N moves down a distance of 50cm at X.
How far upwards is the load lifted at Y?

b) The brakes of a car make use of a hydraulic system.
Using a simple diagram, explain how the car braking system works.

Q3 The pressure in a liquid is often produced by having a "head of liquid". Using this idea, explain the following examples. It will help to draw a picture each time.

a) The water comes out of the hot water tap under pressure.

b) When you swim under water, you feel the extra pressure on your ear drums.

c) When a patient in hospital is given a saline drip or blood transfusion,
the liquid needs to be under pressure when it is injected into the patient.

d) A mercury barometer can be used to measure the pressure of the air.

How Levers Work

Q1 A lever is a simple device that uses a pivot to increase the size of the turning effect of a force.
Copy the following diagrams and label the position of the **pivot** with a **P**.
Draw a line with an arrow to show where the **force is applied** and label it **F**.
Draw a line with an arrow to show where the **force is finally produced** and label it **R**.
The first one is done for you.

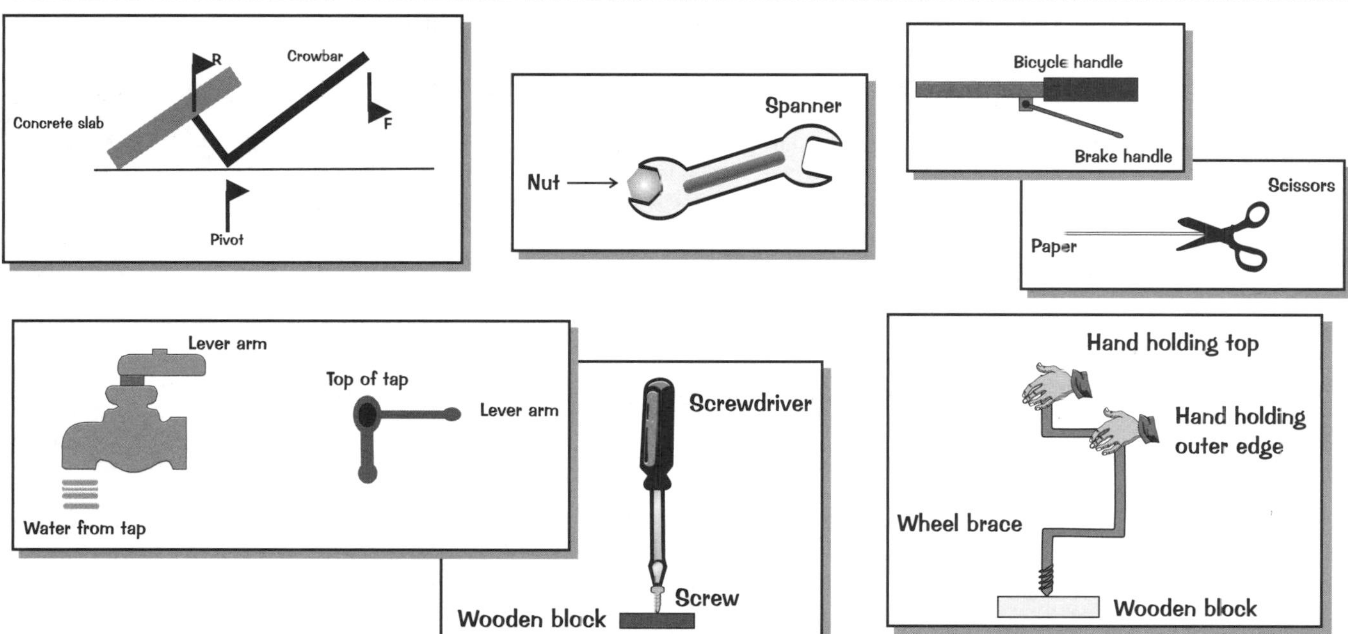

a) Underneath each diagram, explain how the turning effect of the force is increased.

b) Write out a list of five different examples of devices in your home that use a lever and explain for each one how the turning effect of the force is increased.

Q2 The body contains examples of levers. One example is the two muscles in the upper arm.

a) Copy out the following sentences using the correct words.

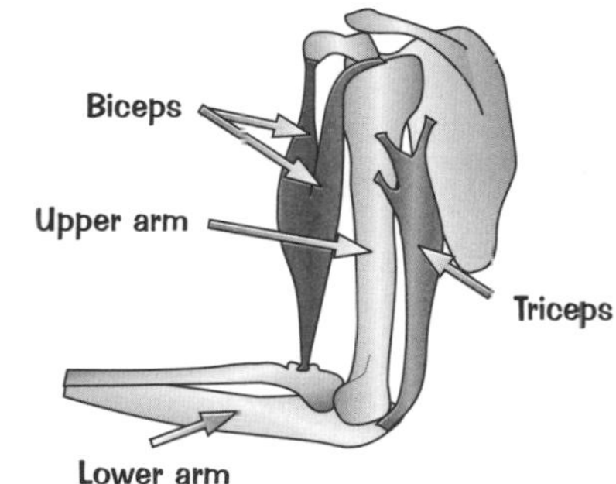

i) A muscle can only **[push/pull]**.

ii) Muscles like the biceps and triceps work **[in pairs/singly]**.

iii) When the biceps muscle **[contracts/relaxes]**, the triceps muscle relaxes and the lower arm is lifted upwards.

iv) When the triceps muscle **[contracts/relaxes]**, the biceps muscle relaxes and the lower arm is moved downwards.

v) The lower arm pivots about the **[elbow joint/the wrist joint]**.

b) Find out about another pair of muscles in the body and explain how they work together. Draw a diagram to help illustrate your answer.

Lever me alone...

Archimedes said, "Give me but one firm spot on which to stand and I will move the earth". I don't know about that but levers are definitely pretty useful for moving smaller things like nuts and taps.

How Things Balance

Q1 Jane and her friend Sophie sit on opposite sides of a see-saw. Jane weighs 500N and Sophie weighs 400N.

a) In each of the situations described, say whether the see-saw would be balanced or which way it would tip. Draw a diagram for each part of your answer.

i) Jane sits 2m from the pivot and Sophie sits 1m from the pivot.

ii) Jane sits 1m from the pivot and Sophie sits 2m from the pivot.

iii) Jane sits 1.5m from the pivot and Sophie sits 2m from the pivot.

iv) Jane sits 1m from the pivot and Sophie sits 1.25m from the pivot.

b) Jane's little brother who weighs 300N sits on her knee. Sophie sits 2m from the pivot. Where would Jane and her brother sit to balance the see-saw?

Q2 The turning effect of a force about a pivot is known as its **moment**.

a) Explain how you would work out the moment of a force about a pivot.

b) A force of 5N acts 1m from a pivot. What is the size of the moment of the force?

c) A force of 100N acts 5m from a pivot. What is the moment of the force?

Q3 A pupil carried out an investigation into balancing using a metre ruler and some 1N weights. The pivot is placed at the centre of the ruler each time.

a) Copy out the diagrams of the different experiments that the pupil did. On each diagram, draw the position of a 1N weight that would cause the rule to balance. Make sure you write down the distance of the 1N weight from the pivot each time.

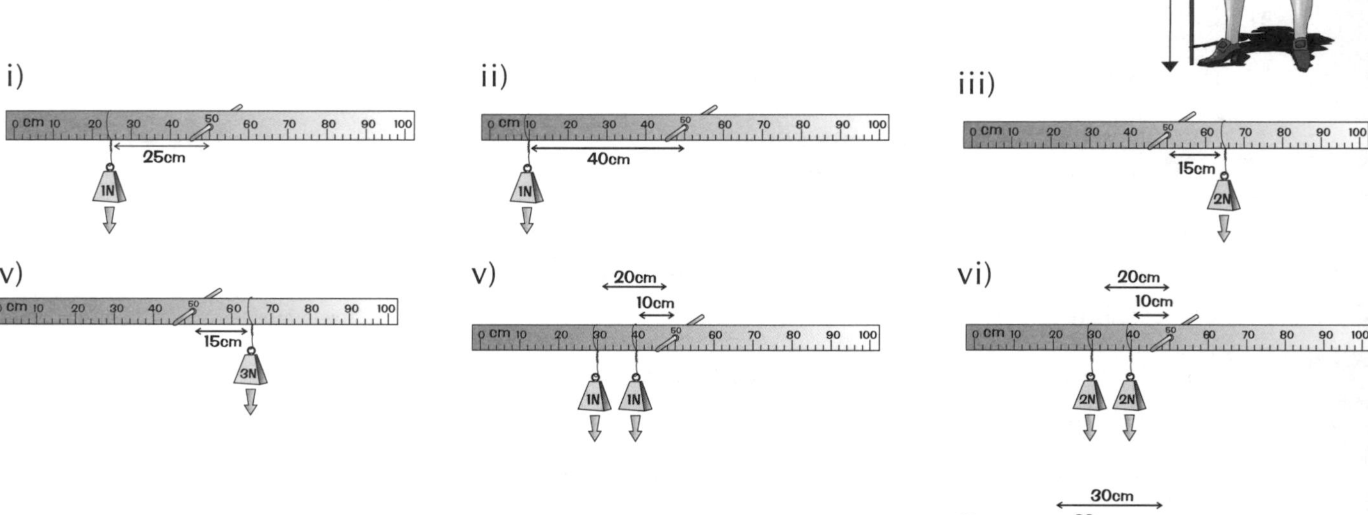

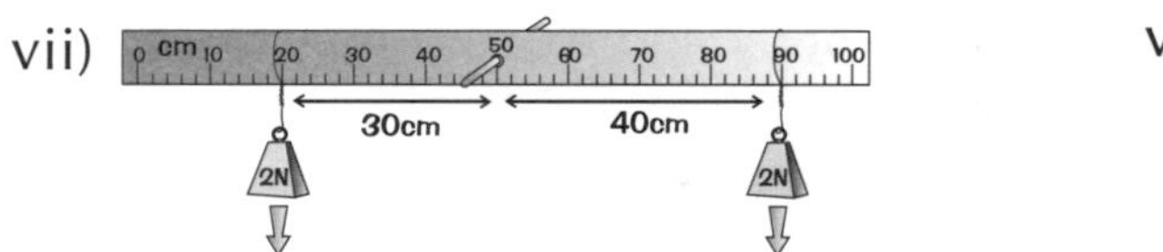

b) Write down in your own words a rule for the forces and their moments when the ruler is balanced.

Scientific Investigations

Q1 From the list below, write down **two** questions which are **not** suitable for scientific enquiry:

At a respected water company...

It's revolting, but it could be worse. Add MORE chlorine.

But sir...

Just do it, Hopkins... Moah ha ha ha. Ha ha ha...

a) How much of a carrot is water?

b) Why do water companies add chlorine to water?

c) Which is the highest waterfall in the UK?

d) Which is the most beautiful lake in the world?

e) How much sweat comes out of a professional footballer during a match?

f) Which tastes better — bottled water or tap water?

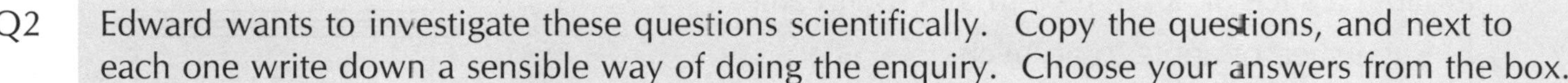

Q2 Edward wants to investigate these questions scientifically. Copy the questions, and next to each one write down a sensible way of doing the enquiry. Choose your answers from the box.

a) Which makes muddy water cleaner — filtering it through sand or filter paper?

b) How can we classify freshwater fish?

c) Where in the UK did it rain most last month?

d) How much water is in a bottle of hair shampoo?

e) Which cools down quicker — a short-haired cat or a long-haired cat?

f) How many daisies are on the school field?

do a survey outside | do an experiment at school | contact the manufacturer | set up a model and collect data from it | use a book from the library | use the internet

Q3 Alison wants to do experiments to investigate these questions. Copy the questions, and next to each one write down **two** things she must do to make sure the experiment is **fair**.

a) Which of these balls bounces highest — a tennis ball, a cricket ball or a table tennis ball?

b) Which type of exercise makes your heart beat fastest — skipping, sprinting or dancing?

c) Which absorbs more sweat — a T-shirt made from cotton or a T-shirt made from polyester?

Q4 Write instructions for a fair test to find out whether more sugar dissolves in hot water or in cold water. Include in your answer:

a) A precise question to investigate.

b) What to do.

c) What measurements to take.

d) What to keep the same to make the experiment fair.

If you thought this page was exciting, wait till you see page 77...

So the first step of a scientific investigation is deciding <u>how</u> you're going to do it. Not all investigations involve playing with test tubes in a lab, which is a shame. (Only 1 page before page 77 now!)

Investigating Water Content of Fruit

Q1 Mary wants to compare the amounts of water in different fruits. Write down **one** question from the list below which she could **not** investigate by doing a fair test:

a) What are the percentages of water in an apple, an orange and a peach?
b) Which taste better — fruits with more water or fruits with less water?
c) Which contains more water — a grape or a mango?
d) Is there more water in 100g of banana or in 100g of pineapple?

Q2 Mary can think of 3 ways of finding out the mass of water in a slice of apple. Copy the 3 sentences and next to each one write down one or more possible hazards.

(Hazards to choose from: **burns**, **hot liquid in eye**, **cuts**, **poisoning**)

a) Hold a slice of apple next to a bunsen flame.
b) Put a slice of apple in an oven.
c) Put a slice of apple in a glass desiccator next to a chemical which absorbs water easily.

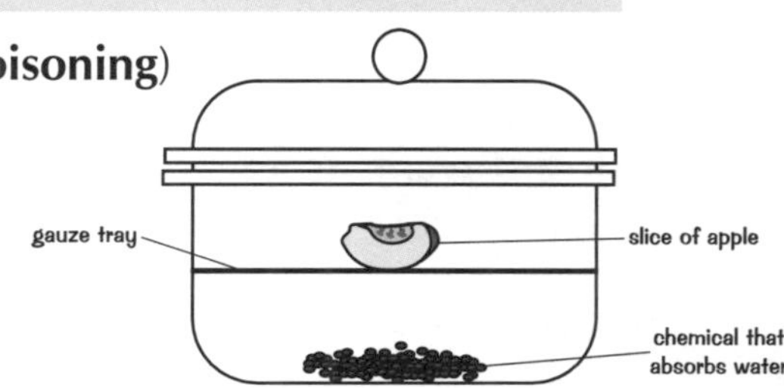

Q3 Mary heated 3 slices of fruit in an oven. She measured the mass of each slice every 15 minutes until the masses didn't change any more. Here are her results:

Time (minutes)	Mass (grams)		
	Apple	Orange	Peach
0	32	30	24
15	30	28	22
30	21	22	15
45	14	17	8
60	10	14	4
75	7	12	3
90	6	11	2
105	5	10	2
120	5	9	2
135	5	9	2

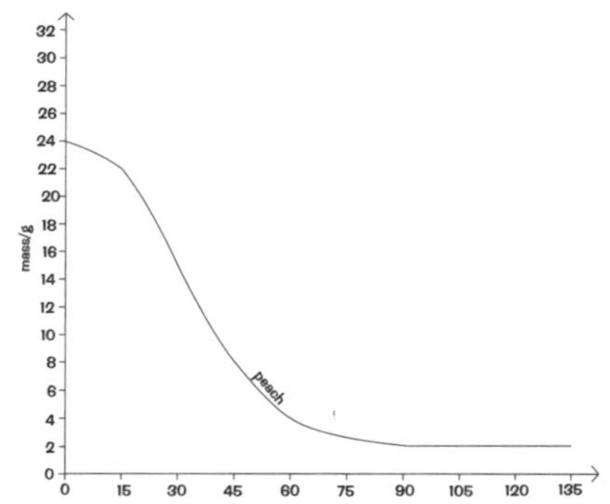

a) Copy the axes and the line graph for the peach slice.
b) Plot the results for the apple and orange slices on the same graph. Draw a smooth curve for each fruit.

Q4 Mary calculated the percentage of water in her apple slice like this:

$$\% \text{ water in apple} = \left(\frac{\text{mass before heating} - \text{mass after heating}}{\text{mass before heating}}\right) \times 100\%$$
$$= \left(\frac{32 - 5}{32}\right) \times 100\%$$
$$= 84\%$$

a) Calculate the percentage of water in the orange.

b) Calculate the percentage of water in the peach.

Q5 Mary calculated that her orange slice was 70% water. A website states that oranges are 87% water. Which **one** statement below could **not** be a reason for this difference:

a) Mary tested a different variety of orange from the one on the website.
b) Mary burnt away some of her orange.
c) Mary left the peel on her orange slice.
d) Mary made a mistake in her calculation.
e) Mary's orange had been in a fruit basket for two weeks.

Investigating How Elephants Cool Down

Q1 Barney wants to know why elephants throw water over themselves. He thinks it might be to help them cool down. He sets up this experiment, and measures the temperature every 2 minutes as the water cools.

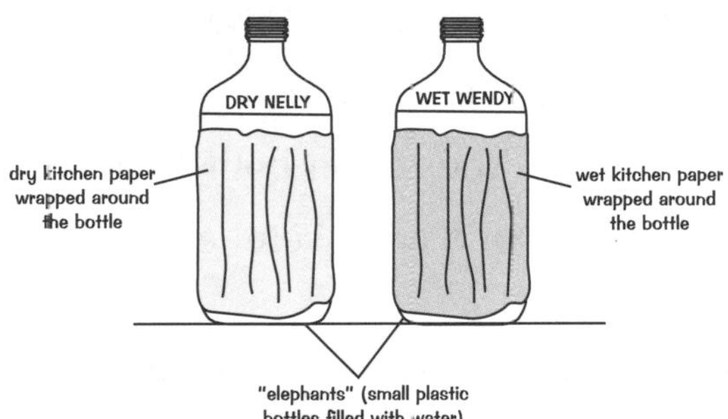

a) Write down **three** things Barney must do to make the experiment **fair**.

b) Write **one** sentence to tell Barney the best starting temperature for the water. Choose from:

i) 100°C because this will cool quickest.

ii) 25°C because this is the temperature of the air where elephants live.

iii) 38°C because an elephant's body temperature is 36-37°C.

c) Barney has 3 different types of thermometer. Copy their names and, for each one, use words from the box to write down an advantage of using it in this experiment.

i) A forehead 'fever thermometer'

ii) A temperature sensor attached to a computer

iii) An alcohol in glass thermometer

it is very accurate

it can easily measure the temperature on the bottle's surface

most schools have plenty of them

Q2 Here is Barney's graph:

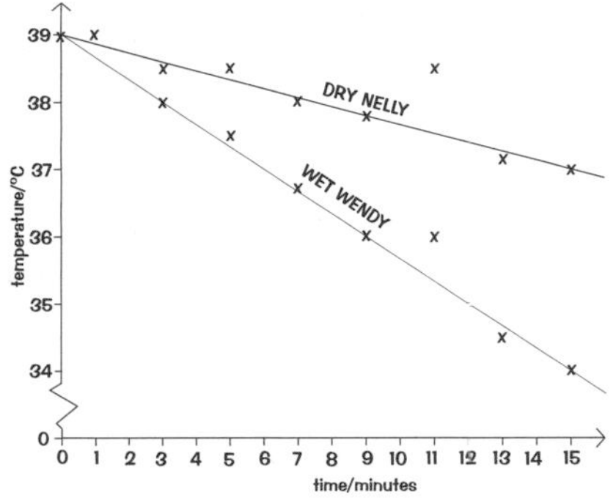

a) Which elephant cooled quicker — Wet Wendy or Dry Nelly?

b) When do you think Barney made a mistake in reading the thermometer?

Q3 Copy the writing and use words from the grey box to fill in the gaps.

faster water heat urine evaporate

Elephants cool down by giving out _____ energy through their skin. If an elephant is wet, heat energy is transferred more quickly to make the water_____. This is why wet elephants cool down _____ than dry elephants. Sometimes elephants spray themselves with mud, or even a mixture of sand and their own _____. The elephants cool down when the _____ from the mud or urine evaporates.

Investigating Soil Moisture Levels

Q1 Copy the writing and fill in the gaps using the words given:

Words to use: dry, sunlight, variety, fair, pH

Grace thinks that a greater _____ of types of plant (plant species) grow in wetter parts of the school field. She does an experiment to find out. She must choose a wet part and a _____ part of the field to study. To make the experiment_____, she must make sure that both areas get the same amount of_____. The soil in both areas must have the same _____ — it would not be fair if the soil in one area were less acidic than the other.

Q2 Copy the writing below, but choose only the **correct** highlighted word each time.

Grace **threw/placed** a quadrat on the ground in the wet area. She **identified/looked at** the plant species in the quadrat. She did this **once/many times** in the wet area to make sure her results were reliable. She then repeated the whole experiment in the **wet/dry** area.

Q3 Answer the following questions about the experiment:

a) What is the one thing that Grace **changed** in her experiment (the **independent** variable)?

b) What did Grace **measure** in her experiment (the **dependent** variable)?

Q4 Here are the results from Grace's experiment:

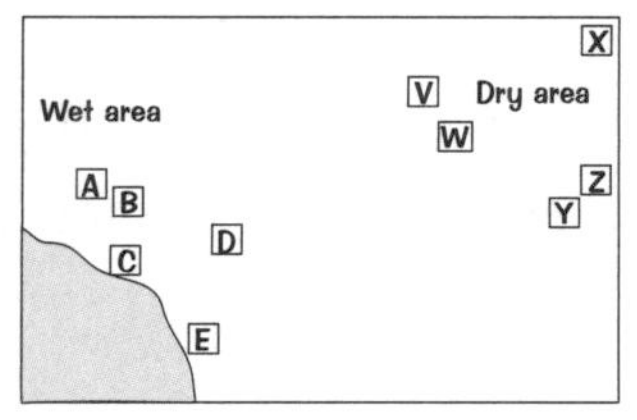

Name of plant species	Is this species present in square...				
	A	B	C	D	E
Grass	✓	✓	✓	✓	✓
Moss	✓	✓	✓	✓	✓
Buttercup	✓	✓	✓	✓	✓
Dock				✓	
Selfheal		✓			✓
Bittercress			✓	✓	
Sorrel	✓	✓	✓		✓
Speedwell		✓			✓
Number of species in this square	4	6	5	5	6

Name of plant species	Is this species present in square...				
	V	W	X	Y	Z
Grass	✓	✓	✓	✓	✓
Moss	✓	✓	✓	✓	✓
Buttercup	✓				
Daisy				✓	
Number of species in this square	3	2	2	3	2

a) Write down the names of the 6 plant species Grace found in square B.

b) How many plant **species** are in square C?

c) Write the names of the 3 plant species in square Y.

d) How many plant **species** are in square W?

e) The average number of plant species in a dry area square is:

$(3 + 2 + 2 + 3 + 2) \div 5 = 12 \div 5 = 2.4$

Calculate the average number of plant species in a wet area square.

f) On average, are there more plant species in a dry area square or a wet area square?

Q5 Grace concluded from her experiment that a greater variety of plant species live in wet areas than in dry areas. Suggest **two** things Grace could do to be more certain that her conclusion is correct.

Classification Systems

The questions on this page are about the plants and algae in these boxes:

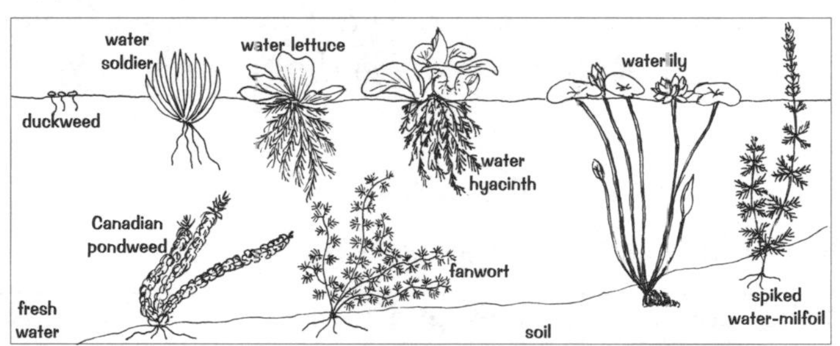

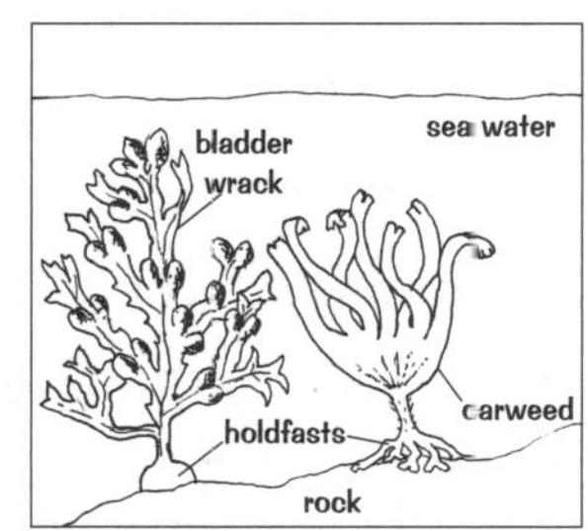

Q1 Lalita used roots and holdfasts to classify the plants.

a) Write down the names of 8 plants with roots. This is **group A**.

b) Write down the names of 2 plants with holdfasts. This is **group B**.

Q2 Lalita decided that **group A** was too big. She split it into 2 smaller groups.

a) Write down the names of 4 'free floaters' whose roots hang down in the water. **(Group C)**

b) Write down the names of 4 plants from group A whose roots are anchored in the soil under the water. This is **group D**.

c) From **group C** write down the names of: i) 1 plant which has long, unbranched roots hanging down to balance it; ii) 2 plants which have bundles of trailing feathery roots to absorb nutrients from the water efficiently.

Q3 Philip used leaves and fronds to classify the plants.

a) Write down the names of 5 plants with floating leaves. This is **group L**.

b) Write down one way in which the leaves of **group L** plants are similar to each other.

c) Write down the names of 5 plants whose leaves or fronds are under the water (submerged). This is **group M**. How are their leaves similar?

Q4 Philip decided that **group M** was too big. He split it into 3 groups: **group N** for plants adapted to life in fast-flowing water; **group P** for plants adapted to life in the sea; **group Q** for plants which live in still or slow-moving water.

a) Name 2 plants in **group N**. They have very narrow leaves so that fast-flowing water can easily slide past them.

b) Name 2 plants in **group P**. They have floppy fronds to swish around in the waves.

c) Name 1 plant in **group Q**.

Q5 Lalita and Philip tried out their classification systems with 2 plants: waterlily (see diagram at top of page) and starwort (see diagram below).

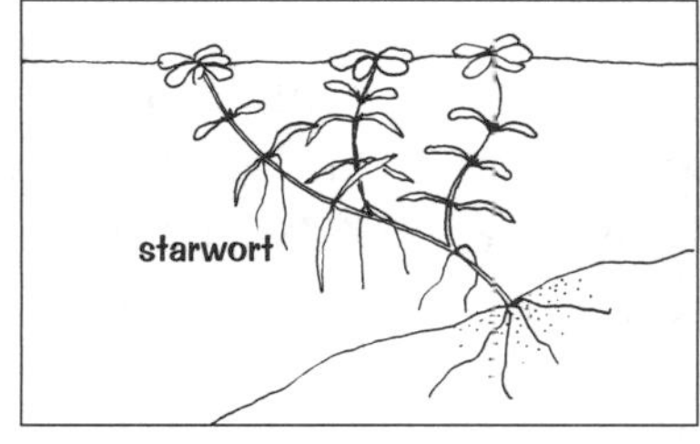

a) Starworts have 2 sorts of leaves. Would Philip put it in **group L**, **group N, group P** or **group Q**? Why?

b) Philip decided that waterlilies belong to **group L**. Would Lalita put them in **group C** or **group D**? Why?

Investigating the pH of Rainwater

Q1 When sulphur dioxide and nitrogen oxides dissolve in rain, the rain is acidic. Acid rain has a pH less than 7. Finish the sentences to create 3 hypotheses which might explain why the pH of rain varies. Choose from the endings in the box.

a) Rain is more acidic near big cities

b) Rain is more acidic when the wind comes from the east

c) Rain is less acidic if it has been raining heavily for several days

because there are many coal-burning power stations in Europe to the east of the UK.	because cars produce lots of nitrogen oxide gases.	because the extra rain dilutes the acid.

Q2 Tom decided to use **secondary sources** (eg books and the internet) to investigate one of the hypotheses in Q1. Copy the table and write 3 of these phrases in each column:

Advantages of using secondary sources	Disadvantages of using secondary sources

a) It takes less time and effort to collect data

b) There may be no data for the place you are interested in

c) It doesn't matter if it doesn't rain when you want to get the information

d) You don't know if you can rely on the people who tested the pH

e) There may be no data for the weeks you are interested in

f) It is easy to get data for enough weeks to spot a trend

Q3 Tom found this data on the internet. It was collected in Yorkshire:

Date	Rainfall (mm)	Rain pH
24 February	19	5.3
9 March	6	4.7
12 October	30	5.9
16 November	16	5.0
21 December	26	5.5

a) Copy the axes and plot the points to make a scatter graph. Do not include the dates! The first point is already on the graph:

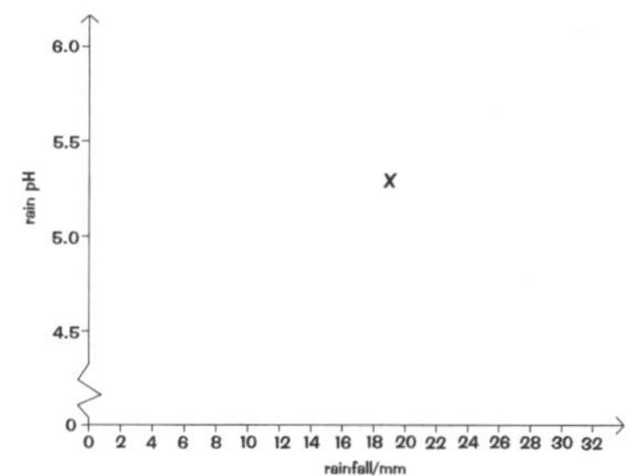

b) Draw a line of best fit.

c) Copy and complete this sentence: The graph shows that the more it rains, the _____ the pH and the _____ acidic the rain.

Q4 Freya noticed that Tom had missed out the data from some weeks. She added some of the missing data to his graph:

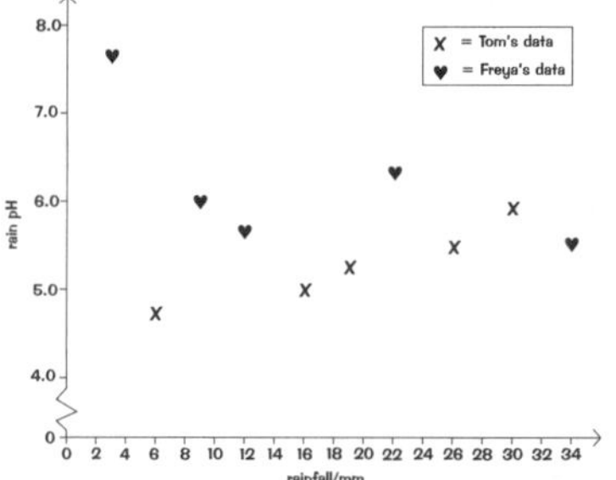

Freya told Tom that there is no relationship between the amount of rain and the rain's pH, but Tom thought there was. Write down whether you agree with Tom or Freya. Give a reason for your answer.

The Answers

Page 1

Q1 a) Things about Sarah which are likely to be **inherited** include hair colour, eye colour and freckles

b) Things about Sarah which are likely to be **environmental** (not inherited) include hair length, musical taste, pierced ears, favourite programme

c) One thing which is likely to be decided by a mixture of inherited **and** environmental factors could be any of height, weight, sporting ability, maths ability

Q2 Things you would expect to be the same for the new tree (when it has grown) and the old tree are:
SHAPE OF LEAVES
COLOUR OF LEAVES
COLOUR OF FLOWERS

Q3 a) TRUE e) FALSE
b) FALSE f) TRUE
c) FALSE g) FALSE
d) TRUE h) TRUE

Q4

Animal	Plant
EGG (OVUM)	EGG (OVUM)
OVARY	OVULE in OVARY
SPERM	POLLEN GRAIN
TESTES	ANTHER
SPERM nucleus joins with EGG nucleus	POLLEN nucleus joins with EGG (OVUM)
EMBRYO	SEED containing EMBRYO

Page 2

Q1 a) The frequency table should be drawn with a line representing each mass in that category. The figures have been included below to show how they divide up.

Mass (g)	110-114	115-119	120-124	125-129	130-134
Frequency	111g	115g 119g	122g 123g 124g	127g 128g	133g

135-139	140-144	145-149	150-154	155-159	160-164
	143g	147g 149g	151g 153g 154g	155g 158g	162g

b)

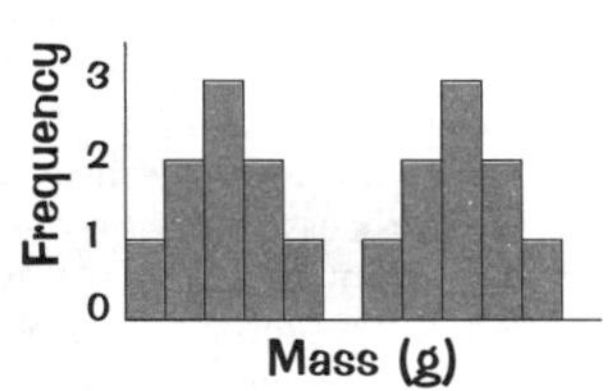

c) There are two varieties as there are two separate distributions.

d) 9

e) It was the same

f) For the potatoes variation **between** the varieties was greater than variation **within** the varieties.

g) diameter, length, colour, taste, skin texture, cooking time

Q2 a) TRUE d) FALSE
b) FALSE e) TRUE
c) TRUE

Q3 a) SIZE, MASS, BEHAVIOUR, HEALTH

b) Any from FOOD PROVIDED , SHELTER PROVIDED, AMOUNT OF HUMAN CONTACT, VETERINARY ATTENTION

c) ENVIRONMENTAL.

Page 3

Q1 a) <u>**JOB**</u>
RETRIEVING GAME
CHASING HARES
HERDING SHEEP
GETTING HUNTED ANIMALS OUT OF THEIR DENS
COMPANION
CARRIAGE DOG
GUARD DOG

b) i) Select his largest dogs and bitches and mate them. Select the largest offspring to continue breeding from.
ii) Selective breeding
iii) Mate dogs with the same parents as this makes it more likely that any genetic defects will show up.

c) i) An inherited characteristic is controlled by **genes**.
ii) Genes are contained in the genetic material in a cell's **nucleus**.
iii) Sex cells contain **half** the genetic material of a body cell.
iv) Sexual reproduction involves two **sex** cell nuclei joining together
v) **Selective** breeding relies on desirable characteristics being passed on in the **genes** in the sex cell's **nucleus**.

Page 4

Q1 a) Beef cattle: faster growth rate, more meat produced, less fat on the meat

b) Dairy cattle: higher milk yield

c) Sheep produced for meat: faster growth rate, more meat produced, less fat on the meat

d) Sheep produced for wool: more wool, whiter wool

e) Pigs: more meat

Q2 They need high quality grazing which depends on high rainfall.
They are used to a temperate climate and would not do well in extreme heat.
They have no resistance to diseases and parasites which occur in Africa.

Q3 a) Disease resistance

b) If the cattle do not survive or are very unhealthy they will not produce milk or meat

c) Drugs

d) Drugs are expensive, drugs may not be easy to obtain in certain areas, microbes can become resistant to drugs

e) There are many crosses that can be tried which will give different results so there is more chance of producing individuals with increased resistance.

Page 5

Q1
- Pollen is made in an anther.
- Pollen is taken from the anther by insects or the wind.
- Some pollen grains reach a stigma in another plant
- Pollination is complete
- The pollen grain germinates and grows a pollen tube
- This grows down through the carpel and into the ovule
- The pollen cell nucleus travels down the tube
- The pollen cell nucleus joins with the ovum
- Fertilisation is complete
- The fertilised ovule becomes a seed

Q2 A 4 D 2
B 5 E 3
C 1

Q3 a) The reason for **selective** pollination is **to control which plants are allowed to pollinate**

b) Cover shoots with buds on before flowers open to prevent natural pollination.

Collect pollen on a paint brush to transfer to a particular stigma.

Remove male plants before the flowers open if there are separate male and female plants to prevent them from pollinating nearby females

Plant only female plants in an area if there are separate male and female plants to prevent natural pollination

Page 6

Q1 a) Mass, diameter, colour, taste, cooking time, taste after freezing

b) Use 50
5 - not enough for a reliable result
5000 - too many to measure

c) i) Peas of variety A are MOSTLY SMALLER than those of variety B.
ii) Peas of variety A are ALWAYS SMALLER than those of variety C.
iii) Peas of variety B are MOSTLY SMALLER than those of variety C.
iv) Peas of variety C are ALWAYS LARGER than those of variety A and are MOSTLY LARGER than those of variety B.

Q2 Same number of peas in each sample.
Same amount of water in each beaker.
Make sure water is boiling in all three

The Answers

beakers before peas are added.
Make sure water remains boiling (might need a trial run to find out how much water is necessary to make this happen).
Remove test peas at the same time.
Test in exactly the same way for each pea.

Q3 a) C
b) The taste results for B and C are very close, probably no real difference
B has a shorter cooking time
B is smaller some people prefer smaller peas
If you've been very clever and looked back at the graph you will see that B also has the least variation in diameter.

Page 7

Q1 Clones are individuals who are genetically **identical**. A clone is produced by **asexual** reproduction. Cloning has been carried out with **plants** for many years. Variation in adult clones will still happen because of **environmental** factors.

Q2 a) FALSE c) TRUE
b) FALSE d) TRUE

Q3 a) Example answers: eye colour, favourite music
b) Fertilisation is the joining of a nucleus from a male sex cell with the nucleus of a female sex cell.
c) i) Sexual reproduction results in offspring which are genetically **similar** but not **identical** to the parents.
ii) Asexual reproduction results in offspring which are genetically **identical** to the **parent**.
iii) **Environmental** factors can cause **variation** even in genetically identical individuals.
iv) **Selective** breeding is used to produce desirable characteristics in animals and plants.
d) Fertilisation
e) Variation
f) Nucleus
g) Carpel
h) Seed
i) Gene
j) Tail

Page 8

Q1 E

Q2 True

Q3 Answers might include: exercise, smoking, diet, alcohol

Q4 different, pulse rate, slowly, quickly

Q5 They should have found several bits of advice about fitness from different sources.

Q6

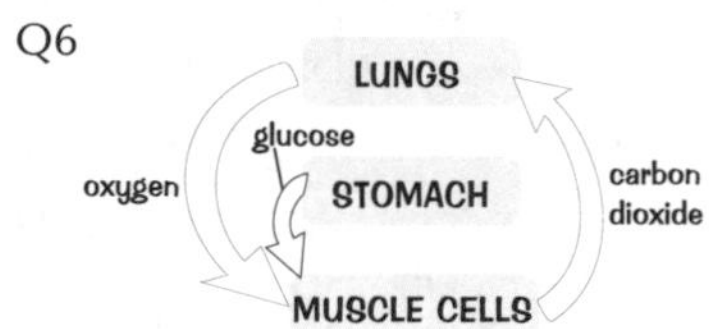

Q7 glucose, water

Page 9

Q1 a) the lungs b) the rib cage c) the intercostal muscles (rib muscles) and the diaphragm d) bronchi/bronchioles e) oxygen f) carbon dioxide and water

Q2 a) it moves up and out b) it moves down and in c) it increases d) it decreases

Q3 a) diaphragm b) trachea c) heart
d) ribs e) intercostal muscle
f) alveoli g) bronchus

Q4 **B** is true.

Q5 Nope. Depends on activites being done and state of health and fitness.

Q6 e.g. exercise, playing a brass instrument...

Page 10

Q1 nicotine, tar, carbon monoxide

Q2 a) The cilia waft them up out of the lungs.
b) The mucus doesn't get wafted out.
c) Smoker's cough/phlegmy cough

Q3 Lung cancer - tar. Raised blood pressure - nicotine. Reduced capacity to carry oxygen in blood - carbon monoxide.

Q4 Prevents enough oxygen getting to the baby in the womb — baby could be born small or deformed, or be still-born.

Q5 Nicotine narrows blood vessels. The heart has to beat faster to get oxygen around the body. Fast blood flow in narrow blood vessels increases blood pressure.

Q6 Nicotine is addictive.

Q7 a) breathing someone else's smoke
b) £748.25
c) It was more acceptable then because people were not aware of the risks.
d) To discourage smoking/to help pay for some of the cost of treating illness caused by smoking.

Q8 Any sensible answer with reference to the different smoking-related illnesses.

Page 11

Q1 carbohydrate, protein, fat, vitamins and minerals

Q2 a) scurvy
b) poor eyesight
c) rickets
d) poor bones and teeth

Q3 Skin-and-bones appearance, with a swollen pot-belly

Q4 a) Body gets fat, fat is deposited inside the arteries, raising blood pressure and putting strain on the heart. Putting on a lot of weight makes it harder to exercise, as you become tired quickly.
b) Constipation, vitamin deficiencies, also may be at greater risk of cancer.
c) Increased blood pressure.

Q5 a) Any 3 from the following: weight gain/ eventual damage to their circulatory system/ at risk from nutrient deficiencies/ possible bad skin from all the greasy food / probably be sluggish and slow and find it hard to exert themselves
b) Any 3 from the following: probably be thin and tired/ won't be able to exercise because they have no energy/ skin may become greyish, dry and dull/ girls might eventually find that their periods stop.

Q6 a) Pellagra is a vitamin B3 deficiency.
b) The rats did not get vitamins.

Page 12

Q1 a) 18 b) yes c) because reactions are slowed and judgement impaired d) yes e) a depressant f) no!

Q2 The liver

Q3 **A** and **C** are true.

Q4 Alcohol damages the fetus

Q5 a) Because excessive drinking of alcohol is dangerous, but moderate drinking is OK for health. Also, alcohol is socially acceptable, so we don't ban it completely
b) For men 28 units/week, for women 21/week.
c) Men are on average heavier, and they process alcohol more quickly than women.
d) No. That amount of alcohol would get you dangerously drunk. Binge drinking is unhealthy.

Q6 People drink most on those nights. Drunk people fall over and/or get into fights, or even pass out, and require medical attention.

Page 13

Q1 a) increases risk of heart attack
b) increases blood pressure

The Answers

c) keeps heart healthy
d) increases blood pressure, puts strain on the heart
e) puts strain on the heart

Q2 Any one of the following: muscles, cartilage, tendons.

Q3 Warm-up exercises and stretching exercises.

Q4 a) Cartilage is worn down.
b) Sensible answers; such as shoulder muscle strengthening execises and warm-up exercises.

Q5 a) strong, same density as bone, long-lasting, uncorrosive...
b) Sensible answers, including different stages of medical and engineering research and development.

Page 14

Q1 a) drug b) drug c) not d) drug e) not f) drug g) drug h) drug

Q2 A substance that changes the way the body or brain works.

Q3

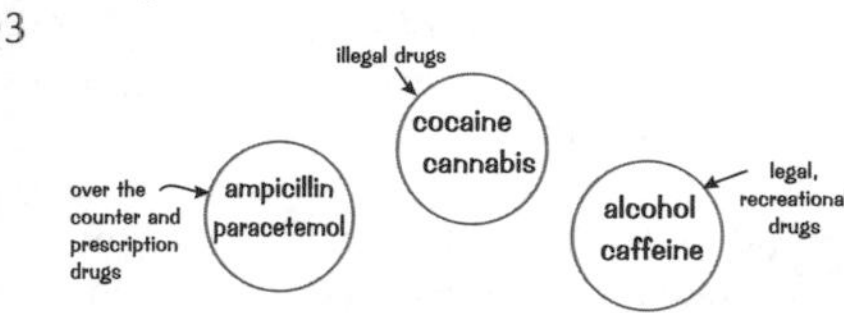

Q4 An effect that isn't the main intended effect of a drug.

Q5 a) So that only the caffeine content was different.
b) Ask if anyone is sensitive/allergic to caffeine, and exclude them from the test.
c) It is.
d) It is.

Page 15

Q1 Any sensible answers, such as internet, history books, interviews...

Q2 Sensible answers, e.g. census data, books, medical journals...

Q3 Sensible answers, e.g. interviews, old films, books and magazines, medical journals...

Q4 Look at old books, films, adverts, interview people...

Q5 Compare information from the internet, modern books, journals, census data etc about modern lifestyles, with information gathered from the sources mentioned in Q1- Q4.

Q6 a) no — they had fewer
b) yes
c) yes

Q7 Any sensible answer.

Q8 Any sensible answer.

Q9 Woman had more children, but fewer lived.

Page 16

Q1 b), d) and e) are true

Q2 a) photosynthesis
b) glucose
c) carbon dioxide and water
d) starch

Q3 Light, chlorophyll and minerals.

Q4 Carbon dioxide + water (+ sunlight & chlorophyll) = glucose + oxygen

Q5 Carbon dioxide is used for photosynthesis in the day, but not at night.

Q6 a) Biomass is all the mass of an organism — all the "stuff" it's made of.
b) New plant biomass is made by photosynthesis.

Page 17

Q1 a) To soften it.
b) To remove the green pigment.
c) green
d) There was starch present.

Q2 The iodine would not turn the leaf blue-black.

Q3 a) Only on the cut out part where the light had reached the leaf surface.
b) So that starch already present in the leaf could be used up.

Q4 The bits that had been green would go black. The white bits would stay white.

Q5 a) chlorophyll.
b) Yes, it's necessary. The experiment with the variegated leaf shows that food is made and stored only in the green parts of the leaf.

Q6 a) Pale and thin and tall and weedy.
b) Etiolation.

Page 18

Q1 oxygen

Q2 a) oxygen
b) It relights a glowing splint.
c) You could use a gas cylinder instead of a test tube and measure the amount of oxygen produced over a certain time.

Q3 **Oxygen** produced by plants is used by plants and animals for **respiration**, which is the process that gets energy from glucose. **Carbon dioxide** produced by this process is used by plants for **photosynthesis**.

Q4 **1.** lots of chloroplasts for photosynthesis/ **2.** tall and thin for maximum chance of light passing through a chloroplast on its way through/ **3.** large surface area to absorb carbon dioxide.

Q5 Photosynthesis is the process used by plants to make their own food.

Page 19

Q1 starch

Q2 respiration

Q3 any sensible answers

Q4 **A** and **C** are true.

Q5 a) fat b) starch c) cellulose d) protein e) sugar f) fat and protein g) cellulose h) cellulose i) starch and protein

Q6 They are al made from glucose.

Page 20

Q1 Support, intake of water, intake of minerals

Q2 Roots need oxygen to function. There needs to be a little air in the soil around a plant, and too much water prevents this.

Q3 large surface area to take in plenty of water and minerals/ thin cell wall for better absorption/ spread out for support

Q4 a) A root hair cell.
b) Root hairs provide an extra large surface area.

Q5 They move up through tubes in the stem.

Q6 You'd see the ink climbing up inside the celery

Q7 a) From the soil.
b) As nitrates.

Q8 To provide added minerals to the soil.

Page 21

Q1 a) photosynthesis uses CO_2 and produces O_2.
b) respiration uses O_2 and produces CO_2.

Q2 a) The concentration of oxygen would go down.
b) The concentration of carbon dioxide would go up.

The Answers

c) Animals would find it harder to survive, as there would be less oxygen to breathe.
d) Photosynthesis and respiration are like opposites. Each one uses the products of the other.

Q3 sensible answers incorporating economical, environmental and medical arguments

Q4

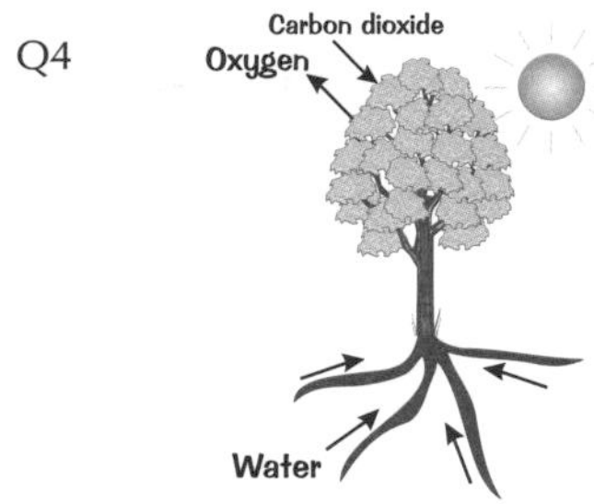

Page 22

Q1 a) sun → grass → lamb
b) sun → grass → cow
c) sun → peach tree
d) sun → wheat
e) sun → potato plant
sun → sunflower
f) sun → carrot
sun → grass → cow
sun → sugar beet/cane
sun → wheat
sun → grain plant → hen
g) sun → potato → pig
sun → grain → chicken → pig
sun → onion → pig
sun → wheat

Q2 a) algae
b) grass
c) wheat

Q3 a) fruit g) root
b) root h) fruit
c) seed i) fruit
d) leaves j) seed
e) seed k) stem
f) stem l) leaves (Yes, leaves.)

Q4 Glucose = carbon dioxide + water + energy
Plants sure do respire.

Q5 a) the seed: to provide fuel for the shoot and root to grow
b) the stem: as a store for winter
c) the roots: as a store for winter when leaves die off and there's not so much light.

Q6 Root vegetables are harvested in winter. Plants do less photosynthesising in winter. They store food in their roots in the form of starch to keep them going during winter.

Page 23

Q1 Nitrogen, Phosphorus and Potassium

Q2 Through the roots, dissolved in water.

Q3 Fertiliser can get into rivers and make the plants and algae grow so much that they use up all the oxygen in the water.

Q4 a) Stems are weak, leaves are yellow.
b) The leaves go yellow and die.
c) Phosphate — without it the roots are poor (beaker B).

Q5 Amount of fertiliser given to plants, concentration of fertiliser used, amount of water given to plants, amount of sunlight they get, the soil they're planted in, type of wheat.

Q6 You'd use a large sample size, so the size variations would average out.

Page 24

Q1 A weed is a plant that competes with a crop or garden plant for resources.

Q2 Water, minerals, light and space.

Q3 The animals would compete for the remaining resources. Animal populations that fed on the weed would decrease.

Q4 a) Selective weedkillers kill particular weeds but do not kill grain crops or grass
b) Grain crops have long thin leaves. Weeds have broad leaves.
c) It is very toxic and can cause burns
d) If placed in another container, it may not be obvious what it is (especially dangerous if a food container is used).
e) Some weedkiller may remain in the container and contaminate whatever else you put in it.

Q5 example answer: using quadrats

Q6 a) number of weeds, amount of weedkiller used, amount of water given
b) Keep the amount of water given to the plants, and any fertiliser given, the same.
c) You need to compare the number of weeds left after doing nothing with the number of weeds left after using weedkiller
d) Package information will tell you how long before the weedkiller kills off the weeds

Page 25

Q1 a) example answer: slugs
b) example answer: mice
c) example answer: caterpillars
d) example answer: aphids

Q2 a)

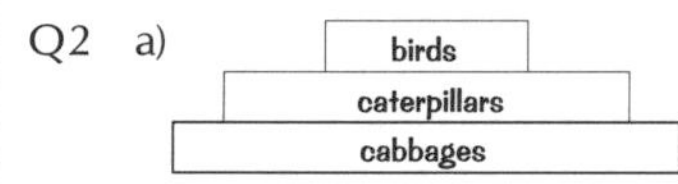

b)

owl
mice
wheat

c)

ladybirds
aphids
tomatoes

Q3 a) slug pellets, beer pits, salt
b) pesticide spray, introduce ladybirds
c) pesticide spray

Q4 a) there'd be fewer
b) there'd be fewer
c) The number of lettuces would be the same. There'd be fewer slugs and thrushes in the one for after pellets.

Page 26

Q1 Through contaminated plants.

Q2 a) It will increase.
b) It would increase.
c) Animals at the top.
d) bioaccumulation

Q3 a) Sensible answer showing knowledge of bias.
b) Sensible answer with justification.
c) Sensible answer.

Q4 Biomanagement — introduction of natural predators, different planting practices.

Page 27

Q1 light, carbon dioxide, water, minerals, warmth

Q2 a) You can control all of them. It's easiest to control warmth, minerals and water.
b) Any sensible answer eg: Putting the plants in a greenhouse to control temperature. Extra watering. Adding minerals to the soil.

Q3 a) You can control the environment, and keep the plants warm and well watered
b) It's expensive to build greenhouses and maintain the plant management systems.
c) The cost of greenhouses outweighs the benefit in quality and quantity of yield.

Q4 Sensible diagram of a greenhouse, with labels for things like light, water and heat control systems.

Q5 Two sensible paragraphs showing understanding of damage caused by agricultural development on the one hand, and the need for cheap plentiful food on the other.

Q6 This is the formal definition: "Sustainable development meets the

The Answers

needs of today's population without harming the ability of future generations to meet their own needs." In other words development without mucking up the environment.

Page 28

Q1 The missing words are:
good, thermal energy, electrical charge, easily, poor.

Q2

Metal	A use	Property
Gold	Jewellery	It doesn't tarnish
Iron	Hammer head	It is hard
Copper	Electric wires	Good electrical conductor
Silver	Candlesticks	Shiny
Zinc	Galvanizing	Stops iron rusting
Lead	Covering roofs	Easily beaten into shape

Q3 a) silver, copper, gold, zinc, iron, lead, graphite, sulfur, oxygen.
b) graphite.
c) silver, copper, gold, graphite, zinc, iron, lead, sulfur, oxygen.
d) Metals are generally good conductors of electricity and heat whilst non-metals are bad conductors. One exception to this rule is graphite.

Q4 Any reasonable use of the words:
hard, flexible, shiny, strong, conductors, heat, electricity, easy to shape.

Page 29

Q1 The missing words are:
hydrogen gas, salt, dissolves, hydrogen gas, squeaky pop.

Q2 The missing words are:
iron sulfate,
iron chloride,
magnesium sulfate,
magnesium,
calcium, hydrochloric acid,
sulfuric acid,
hydrogen,
lead, hydrogen,
lead, hydrochloric acid, hydrogen.

Q3

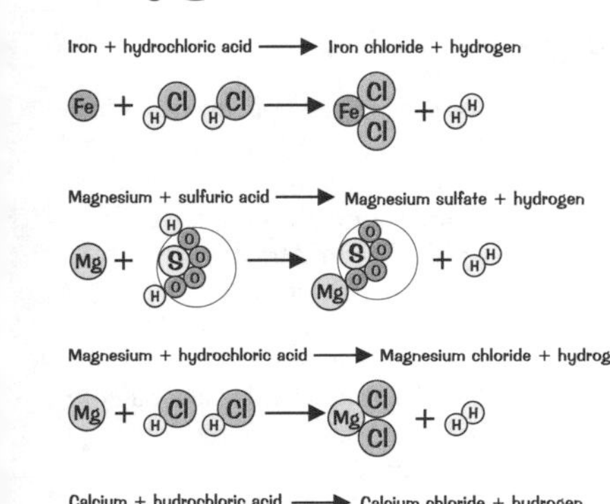

Tin + sulfuric acid → Tin sulfate + hydrogen

Tin + hydrochloric acid → Tin chloride + hydrogen

Lead + sulfuric acid → Lead sulfate + hydrogen

Lead + hydrochloric acid → Lead chloride + hydrogen

Page 30

Q1 The missing words are:
carbonate, acid, chemical reaction, bubbles, carbon dioxide, warmer, dissolve.

Q2 a) Carbon dioxide
b) Turn Milky (not cloudy)
c) Calcium nitrate
d) It dissolves
e) calcium carbonate + nitric acid → calcium nitrate + carbon dioxide + water

Q3 The missing words are:
c) carbon dioxide
d) zinc, water
e) copper sulfate, carbon dioxide
f) magnesium nitrate, carbon dioxide, water
g) iron, nitric, carbon dioxide, water
h) metal carbonate + acid → salt + carbon dioxide + water

Page 31

Q1 The missing words are:
1) black, colourless, blue, chemical reaction.
2) blue, copper oxide.
3) blue, copper sulfate, chemical reaction.

Q2 The missing words are:
b) zinc chloride
c) water
d) sulfuric acid, water
e) iron oxide
f) Magnesium oxide, nitric acid, water
g) metal oxide + dilute acid → salt + water

Q3 a) The carbonate will produce bubbles of CO_2 with acid.
b) Zinc carbonate + sulfuric acid → zinc sulfate + carbon dioxide + water
Zinc oxide + sulfuric acid → zinc sulfate + water
c) $ZnCO_3 + H_2SO_4 \longrightarrow ZnSO_4 + CO_2 + H_2O$
$ZnO + H_2SO_4 \longrightarrow ZnSO_4 + H_2O$

Page 32

Q1 a) C
b) A and D
c) B and E
d) A and B

Q2 a) Mix equal amounts of acid and alkali. Evaporate water to leave crystals of sodium chloride.
b) Sodium hydroxide + hydrochloric acid → sodium chloride + water
c) Neutralization
d) Safety goggles.

Q3 a) Use potassium hydroxide in place of sodium hydroxide.
b) Potassium hydroxide + hydrochloric acid → potassium chloride + water
c) Safety goggles.

Page 33

Q1 The missing words are:
d) sodium chloride
e) potassium nitrate
f) iron sulfate
g) magnesium hydroxide
h) potassium hydroxide, nitric acid
i) Acid + Alkali → Salt + Water.

Q2

Salt	Use	How it could be made
Sodium stearate	Soap	Sodium hydroxide + stearic acid (in fat)
Potassium nitrate	Fertilizer	Potassium hydroxide + nitric acid
Copper sulfate	Slug pellets	Copper oxide + sulfuric acid
Calcium phosphate	Plant food	Calcium hydroxide + phosphoric acid
Iron sulfate	Iron tablets	Iron oxide + sulfuric acid
Magnesium sulfate	Epsom salts	Magnesium oxide + sulfuric acid
Silver nitrate	Photography	Silver oxide + nitric acid

Page 34

Q1 a) Dissolve magnesium in acid. Filter off any excess magnesium. Evaporate to dryness to obtain magnesium sulfate crystals.
b) Magnesium + sulfuric acid → magnesium sulfate + hydrogen
c) Safety goggles.

Q2 a) Stir the mixture of powders in dilute acid. The carbonate will react, dissolving in the acid and producing bubbles of carbon dioxide gas. Filter off the un-dissolved sulfate. Dry the filtered solution to obtain crystals of calcium chloride.
b) Calcium carbonate + hydrochloric acid → calcium chloride + carbon dioxide + water
c) Add a little acid. If bubbles of CO_2 are observed then the sulfate is contaminated with carbonate.
d) Safety goggles.

Q3 a) To separate the copper oxide from the copper nitrate crystals, put them into water and stir until the copper nitrate has dissolved. Then filter the solution. This will remove the copper oxide as it is insoluble. Then evaporate the water off to leave pure copper nitrate.

The Answers

b) The original experiment could be modified by filtering the solution after step 1 and then evaporating off the remaining liquid (as above).

c) Copper Oxide + Nitric acid ⟶ Copper Nitrate + Water

d) Safety goggles.

Q4 a)

Hydrogen

Sulfuric acid

Iron filings

b) iron + sulfuric acid ⟶ iron sulfate + hydrogen

c) The green crystals left in the barrel are iron sulfate. They get there because when a metal reacts with an acid it produces a salt and hydrogen. This equation shows how it happens.
Iron + sulfuric acid ⟶ iron sulfate + hydrogen
The crystals have several uses. They are good for keeping iron levels in the blood where they should be. They are also used as a plant food etc.

Page 35

Q1 a) Air and moisture makes the metals go dull or dark or tarnish.
b) Gold
c) Gold is not very reactive.
d) Yes, it is unreactive.
e) Iron would react with the moisture on your skin and rust.

Q2 a) iron/steel
b) water and oxygen
c) It is brass and contains the less reactive metal copper.
d) The bayonet in the museum is kept indoors away from water.

Q3 a) left hand side (group I)
b) Metals — they are shiny and metals are on the left of the periodic table.
c) Conduct heat well/conduct electricity well, soft etc.
d) Potassium — it became tarnished the quickest i.e. reacted quickest.
e) The air (oxygen) and water in the air.

Page 36

Q1 a) K, Na (and Mg but reacts best with steam, only v slowly with cold water).
b) K and Na
c) Fe and Mg
d) K, Na, Mg, Fe, Cu

Q2 a) the lithium will react with the water producing bubbles of gas which rise and fill the test tube.
b) X = hydrogen
c) Hydrogen gas produces a squeaky pop when ignited with a lighted splint.
d) UI solution would change to a blue colour.
e) The reaction produces lithium hydroxide which is an alkali.
f) Lithium + Water → Lithium Hydroxide + Hydrogen
g) Same reaction except the sodium would react more violently.

Q3 Potassium metal was put on water in a glass trough. The metal **floated** and then fizzed giving off **hydrogen** gas. The reaction gave off so much heat that the metal **melted** and the gas ignited to produce **a lilac** flame. The reaction produced potassium **hydroxide**, which is alkaline and turns UI solution **blue**.

Page 37

Q1 a) a salt and hydrogen
b) → salt + hydrogen
c) squeaky pop test/lighted splint test

Q2 a)

Metal	Symbol	Reaction with acid	Observations
Copper	Cu	nothing seen	no bubbles
Zinc	Zn	vigorous reaction	quite a lot of bubbles
Iron	Fe	a moderate reaction seen	a few bubbles were seen

b) Zinc
c) It is not very reactive/below hydrogen in the activity series so cannot displace hydrogen from acids.

Q3 a) Zinc + hydrochloric acid → zinc chloride + hydrogen
b) Iron + hydrochloric acid → iron chloride + hydrogen
c) Copper + hydrochloric acid → no reaction
d) (Most reactive first) Zinc, iron, copper
e) They would react in the same way
f) Magnesium + hydrochloric acid → magnesium chloride + hydrogen

Q4 Tinned fruit is acidic and so would react with the iron in the steel, the lining stops this.

Page 38

Q1 When a metal reacts with oxygen it forms a metal **oxide**. This is a **chemical** change or chemical **reaction** which involves the metal chemically **joining** to oxygen. The compound which is made has different **properties** from the metal and the oxygen from which it was formed.

Q2 a) Yes, they seem to react more vigorously in oxygen.
b) Air is only about 21% oxygen so the metals oxidise better in pure oxygen.
c) Mg, Zn, Fe, Cu

Q3 a) Iron + oxygen → Iron oxide
b) Magnesium + oxygen → magnesium oxide
c) Copper + oxygen → copper oxide
d) Zinc + oxygen → zinc oxide

Page 39

Q1 a) Copied into book.
b) i) copper sulfate + lead → lead sulfate + copper
ii) copper sulfate + iron → iron sulfate + copper
iii) copper sulfate + copper → no reaction
iv) copper sulfate + zinc → zinc sulfate + copper

Q2 a) The single polystyrene balls represent the elements and the balls stuck together represent the compounds. He is demonstrating how displacement takes place.
b) i) magnesium ii) zinc
c) Stick = weaker bond or join, the glue is a stronger bond showing that the metal is reactive.
d) Displacement reaction

Q3 The more reactive metal takes the place of the less reactive one in the less reactive metal's compound.

Page 40

Q1 a) It melts the iron.
b) The melted iron finds its way between the tracks of the railway and welds them together when it cools and solidifies.
c) It is more reactive
d) Not a good way, aluminium has a higher melting point than iron and so unlikely to make a good weld.

Q2 a) reacts with iron sulfate only
b) less
c) more
d) yes
e) put the metal between iron and zinc
f) benhiddium + zinc sulfate → no reaction
benhiddium + iron sulfate → benhiddium sulfate + iron
zinc + benhiddium sulfate → zinc sulfate + benhiddium
iron + benhiddium sulfate → no reaction

Page 41

Q1 a) **Sodium:** Areas of salt deposits e.g. Cheshire
Iron: Germany
Aluminium: South Africa
Gold: South Africa
b) **Sodium:** Chloride
Iron: Oxide like haematite and magnetite
Aluminium: Oxide like bauxite
Gold: Metal in quartz veins
c) **Sodium:** 2.5%
Iron: 4%
Aluminium: 7%
Gold: Very little
d) **Sodium:** 1807
Iron: Pre-historic times

The Answers

Aluminium: 1825
Gold: Pre-historic times

e) **Sodium:** Electrolysis in Down's cell
Iron: Smelting with carbon in blast furnace
Aluminium: Electrolysis of melted oxide mixed with cryolite
Gold: N/a

f) **Sodium:** Soft/good conductor of heat/low density
Iron: Magnetic, high tensile strength when alloyed
Aluminium: Hard/low density/ ductile/malleable
Gold: Ductile and malleable/v good conductor

g) **Sodium:** High
Iron: Medium
Aluminium: High (but oxide coating seems to reduce it)
Gold: low

h) **Sodium:** Above C and H
Iron: Above H, below C
Aluminium: Above C and H
Gold: Below C and H

i) **Sodium:** Anti-knocking agents/ coolant in nuclear reactors/making alkalis and Cl_2.
Iron: Construction, magnets, engineering e.g. cars, trains and boats, catalyst in the Haber process, used to make steel and stainless steel.
Aluminium: Aircraft bodies, ladders, window frames, power cables, catalyst.
Gold: Jewellery, currency (gold bullion), dental fillings.

j) **Sodium:** Occasionally.
Iron: Yes to make steels.
Aluminium: Yes, to make stronger.
Gold: Yes, to make harder.

Q2 i) Iron isn't as reactive as other metals like aluminium and sodium, so it's relatively easy to extract.
ii) The extraction is relatively easy, so iron was discovered relatively early.

Q3

Metal	How it is extracted
potassium	electrolysis
sodium	electrolysis
calcium	electrolysis
magnesium	electrolysis
aluminium	electrolysis
zinc	smelting
iron	smelting
tin	smelting
lead	smelting
copper	smelting (+thermal decomposition of sulphide)
silver	found as native metal
gold	found as native metal
platinum	found as native metal

Page 42

Q1 Words in order: higher, activity, displace, smelting, expensive.

Q2 a) A compound is a pure substance made of two or more elements chemically joined together.
b) Reactivity describes how reactive a substance is — how vigorously it reacts
c) React means to undergo a chemical reaction.
d) Salts are compounds that are formed from acids when some or all of the acid's hydrogen is replaced with a metal. An example of a common salt is sodium chloride.
e) An equation shows what happens in a reaction.
f) A reactant is a substance which reacts in a chemical reaction.
g) A product is a substance which is made in a chemical reaction
h) Copper sulfate is a salt made of copper, sulfur and oxygen.
i) Magnesium nitrate is a salt made of magnesium, nitrogen and oxygen.
j) Zinc chloride is a salt made of zinc and chlorine.
k) Elements can be arranged in order of reactivity to compare how reactive they are.
l) Qualitative observations are ones where you describe things instead of making measurements.

Q3 a) A dull red colour would start to appear and orange/brown copper metal would appear in the tube.
b) A permanent colour change has occurred.
c) Copper oxide + iron → copper – iron oxide

Page 43

Q1 a) rock particles
b) minerals
c) air
d) living organisms
e) water
f) humus

Q2 The complete sentences are:
a) Sandy soil contains larger rock particles **so water drains through it quickly**
b) Clay soil has little air in it **so few organisms can live in it**
c) Plant roots hold soil together **which helps to prevent erosion**
d) Humus is dead organic matter in soil **which provides nutrients**
e) Loam is an ideal soil type **because it has good mineral content and drains well**
f) Organisms like worms are vital for soil **because they help to circulate air.**

Q3 a)
ACID — ALKALI
pH
4.5 5.0 5.5 6.0 6.5 7.0 7.5
NEUTRAL

b) i) increase
ii) alkali
iii) potato

Page 44

Q1 a) Tree roots grow through the cracks in the wall, weakening it. Larger roots grow under the wall, pushing stones out of the way.
b) Ice formation causes the cracks to expand then weaken.
c) Walkers may tread on and around the wall damaging it.
d) Acids attack limestone, wearing it away.

Q2 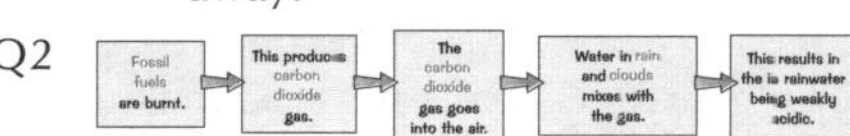

Q3 a) Burning fossil fuels such as coal oil and gas for factories power stations and in vehicles etc.
b) Volcanic eruptions, geysers.

Page 45

Q1 a)

Type of rock tested	Observations over 20 minutes
Granite	no change
Limestone	bubbles of gas, pieces of rock got smaller
Sandstone	bubbles of gas, pieces of rock got smaller

b) i) limestone or sandstone
ii) Church and gravestones have worn away corners, fine pieces of external church architecture worn away, difficult to read words on gravestones, walls and gravestones smooth

Q2 The missing words are: building, metal, corroded, reaction, organisms fish, neutralise.

Page 46

Q1 Answers are subjective.

Q2 a) Evidence which could be collected might include the following:
Interviews with old and young people describing pollution and their environments
Medical records
Environmental / meteorological
Industry / public health records
Emissions data for area (internet)
Asthma sufferers in school
Photographs (e.g. of buildings)
Newspaper articles
Museums
Writings
b) Reliable evidence includes evidence that is unlikely to be biased or inaccurate e.g. Properly conducted questionnaires rather than anecdotal evidence, scientific measurements and data produced by uninterested public bodies, photographs, public records.
c) Main differences between past and present day types of evidence:
Scientific information is more accurate due to better technology and knowledge.
People have more awareness of environmental issues now so they are more likely to understand and challenge information.

The Answers

Much more information is now in the public domain; confusing or useful ?
Internet makes information-seeking relatively easy.

d) Strengths and weaknesses of present-day and past evidence:
<u>Present day</u> - more information. This can either be useful or confusing/contradictory
Information is more accurate due to advancement in science and technology
Information has to be unbiased due to legislation and regulation.
<u>Past</u> - less information available and in simpler form so easier to understand.
Information from fewer sources (environmental groups, regulatory bodies etc.)

Page 47

Q1 The missing words are:
coal, oil, gas, fossil, millions, plants, animals, burning, elements, oxygen, carbon, dioxide, oxides, nitrogen, acidity, pH, carbon, greenhouse, global warming.

Q2 a) Each ring shows a year of growth, the amount of growth depends on temperature
b) There are few direct thermometer measurements before about 1850
c) By comparing growth with direct measurements in recent years.
d) It started rising about 1900 and is still rising.
e) It comes from lots of separate experiments which all show the same thing.
f) Increased levels of greenhouse gases, particularly carbon dioxide from the burning of fossil fuels
g) B, F, G

Page 48

Q1 b, c, e, f, g

Q2 The missing words are:
a) methane
b) vapour, condense
c) milky, dioxide

Q3 The correct words are:
hydrogen, carbon, oxygen, water

Q4 a) carbon dioxide
b) carbon monoxide, carbon

Q5

Advantages of using hydrogen as a fuel	Disadvantages of using hydrogen as a fuel
We can produce hydrogen from water vapour	Hydrogen must be compressed for storage
Hydrogen does not make carbon dioxide when it burns	A mixture of hydrogen and air explodes easily

Page 49

Q1 magnesium, zinc, iron, lead, copper, silver

Q2 The missing words are:
energy, electrical, reactivity, further, series

Q3 The correct words are:
a) smaller
b) more
c) 0.6V
d) lead

Q4 a) magnesium
b) iron and lead
c) silver

Page 50

Q1

Chemical reactions that happen in living things	Chemical reactions that humans do to make useful substances
Making glucose in photosynthesis	Making plastic for mobile phones
Respiration	Cooking chips
Breaking down starch to make glucose	Making salmeterol for asthma inhalers
Making urine	Making potassium chlorate for match heads

Q2 a, c, d, f, g

Q3 The correct order:
B, D, G, C, A, F, E

Page 51

Q1 The missing words are:
solution, powder, 27g, product, conserved

Q2 a) 50g
b) 2g

Q3 The true sentences are:
a, c, d

Q4 a) H–Cl
b) C≡O
c) O=O
d) H–H

Page 52

Q1 The missing words are:
air, increased, oxygen, magnesium

Q2 a) About 0.65g
b) About 0.48g
c) Some of the magnesium oxide powder might have blown away

Q3 a) **H**ydrogen
b) **Y**ou
c) **D**iesel
d) **R**eaction
e) **O**xygen
f) **C**arbon
g) **A**ir
h) **R**ubidium
i) **B**urns
j) **O**nly
k) **N**itrogen

Page 53

Q1 The missing words are:
a) New
b) arrangements
c) conserved, products.

Q2 a) diagram C
b) diagram B
c) diagram A

Q3 a) Equation N
b) Equation M, Equation P
c) Equation Q
d) Equation M, Equation P

Q4 a) arsenic + oxygen ⟶ arsenic oxide
b) nitric acid + magnesium ⟶ magnesium nitrate + hydrogen

Q5 a) $S_{(s)} + O_{2(g)} \longrightarrow SO_{2(g)}$
b) $HCl_{(aq)} + NaOH_{(aq)} \longrightarrow NaCl_{(aq)} + H_2O_{(l)}$
c) $2Mg_{(s)} + O_{2(g)} \longrightarrow 2MgO_{(s)}$

Page 54

Q1 **Nuclear:** The energy released by splitting atoms.
Electrical: The kind of energy carried by charges going around a circuit.
Light: This kind of energy helps you to see where you're going.
Heat or Thermal: Hot objects have plenty of this kind of energy.
Kinetic: A moving train has a lot of this energy.
Chemical: The energy in food, fuels and inside batteries.
Sound: A noisy class is a good source of this.
Elastic Potential: The energy that you need in a catapult.
Gravitational Potential: The energy that you give to something when you lift it into the air.

Q2 a) Loudspeaker - sound
b) Toaster - heat
c) Battery charger - chemical
d) Smoke detector - sound
e) Drill - kinetic
f) Computer screen - light
g) Alarm clock - sound

Q3 These are examples of possible answers:
a) Sound - microphone
b) Chemical - battery
c) Light - solar panel
d) Gravitational Potential - hydroelectric power plant
e) Elastic Potential - wind up radio
f) Kinetic - wind turbine

Q4 a) Car - chemical - fuel tank
b) Grandfather clock - gravitational potential - weights
c) Walkman - chemical - battery
d) Wind up toy - elastic potential - spring
e) You - chemical - food
f) Match - chemical - on the head

Page 55

Q1 <u>Circuit</u>: A complete conducting path which allows something electrical to work.
<u>Closed</u>: The switch contacts are shut together so that a current can flow.
<u>Open</u>: The switch contacts have a gap between them so the circuit is off.
<u>Copper</u>: A good conductor used inside wires.
<u>Insulator:</u> Something which won't conduct electricity.
<u>Battery:</u> Two or more cells joined end to end.
<u>Metre:</u> The metric unit of length.
<u>Current:</u> A flow of electrical charges around a circuit.

The Answers

Currant: A dried up grape that you find in a cake.
Symbol: A black and white line drawing that represents a real component.
Meter: A device for measuring current or voltage.
Terminal: The end of a cell or battery.

Q2 B, C, D, F

Q3 Voltage is measured with a VOLTMETER which must be connected in PARALLEL. Current is measured with an AMMETER which always goes into a circuit in SERIES. It is very difficult to damage a VOLTMETER in a circuit but if it's connected wrongly the circuit won't work properly. If you are trying to measure current and get it wrong by connecting an AMMETER in PARALLEL then it could get DAMAGED.

Q4 a) Zippy

b)

Jane

Rod

Freddie

Page 56

Q1 Model 1
- a) water
- b) pump
- c) water wheel
- d) Electricity doesn't hang about in lakes.

Model 2
- a) skiers
- b) lift
- c) carving snow or crashing
- d) Real skiers can go to other mountains or stop on the way down. Electric currents don't stop part way round.

Model 3
- a) the players
- b) the go space or bank
- c) the squares where money is spent
- d) Players can pay money to each other etc. Electric currents are nothing like Monopoly.

Q2 a) A dry cell contains **chemicals** which are **gradually used up** as the cell supplies electrical energy.
- b) A simple dry cell uses a graphite rod inside a **zinc and steel** case but it isn't very powerful.
- c) Modern high power cells use metals like **lithium and mercury**.
- d) These metals are very **poisonous** so you shouldn't mess about with them.
- e) A cell can be made by sticking pieces of **metal** into a **lemon**.
- f) The citric acid in the lemon dissolves the **metal** and produces a **voltage**.

Q3 a) Prevents pollution. (environment rather than electrical)
- b) Carbon fibre rods conduct electricity.
- c) The machinery is very dangerous even if it is silent or not moving.
- d) TV sets contain components (capacitors) that can hold enough energy to kill you.
- e) Apart from the trains, some lines also have a high voltage rail.
- f) You could get a shock.

Page 57

Q1 a) 230
- b) kWhr (kilowatthour)
- c) watts
- d) energy, power, time, hours
- e) kWhr, power, kilowatt, hour
- f) current, voltage

Q2 clock 20W, light bulb 100W, computer 300W, drill 800W, kettle 1200W, cooker 15000W

Q3 a) 20p d) 50p
b) 30p e) 84p
c) 5p f) 27p

Q4 a) You spend more time indoors with heat and lighting on.
- b) A TV uses more power than a lamp. Also a TV is more complicated inside and has a higher chance of catching fire!
- c) Things that make heat use a lot of electrical energy. Computers do a lot but don't use a lot of power.
- d) Your ears are very sensitive to sound but it takes a lot of energy to warm up a room.
- e) The appliance still uses quite a bit of power even on standby. If you leave it on all the time then this soon mounts up. It is bad for the environment because it increases the burning of fuel in power stations.

Page 58

Q1 Electricity is **generated** in a **power station**. A **transformer** converts it to a very high **voltage** for transmission over the **power pylons**. This **voltage** is far too high to be safe in your house so a **transformer** in a **sub-station** drops the **voltage** down to 230V. This then enters your house at the **consumer unit** where the **meter** measures the amount of energy that your house uses.

Q2 a), e), h) are TRUE,
b), c), d), f), g) are FALSE

Q3

Power Station	Good Points	Bad Points
Wind Turbine	No fuel burnt so no pollution.	Some people think that they are noisy and ugly.
Nuclear	A large amount of energy comes from a small quantity of fuel.	The waste produced is dangerous for thousands of years.
Coal Burning	Plenty of fuel still available.	Causes acid rain and global warming.
Gas Burning	The cleanest of the fossil fuels.	The fuel could run out in less than 50 years.
Tidal	Able to produce power twice every day regardless of the weather.	Could have very bad effects on wading birds.
Hydro-electric	No fuel burnt so no harmful emissions.	Has been linked to earthquakes. Displaces poor people from their farmland.
Biomass	Provides habitat for birds and insects.	Needs a lot of land and good management to be renewable.

Page 59

Q1 a) A lot of energy is used extracting it and raising it to the surface.
- b) More energy is then used to transport the coal to the power station.
- c) Crushing the coal into a fine powder that is blown into the furnaces accounts for a third of the energy that will be obtained from it.
- d) Energy is lost in the steam from the cooling towers. This energy is not used for anything.
- e) Some energy is lost as the power is transmitted long distances over the national grid.
- f) Every electrical appliance in your house wastes some of the energy that it receives.

Q2 a) It takes a lot of energy to make and shape the metal and plastic parts of the car.
- b) A huge amount of energy is used to transport the components.
- c) Electricity wastes a lot of energy in its manufacture and distribution.
- d) Air resistance reduces the car's efficiency therefore wastes energy.

Q3 a) Use less energy. Last longer.
- b) Good for your body, saves energy and cuts pollution.
- c) Less energy is wasted if more people go in trains. If more people used public transport then fewer cars would be needed.
- d) Planes use vastly more energy than any other form of transport.
- e) Save trees! Save Postman Pat's petrol.
- f) Screen savers are pretty but use the machine's full power. Switching off the power cuts your bills and will save the planet!

The Answers

g) Saves on transport costs of raw materials. The recycled stuff is a purer raw material too.

h) Saves the energy costs of the plastic bottle and distribution of the product.

Page 60

Q1 The force of gravity on you is called your **WEIGHT**. This force pulls you towards the **CENTRE** of the Earth. If you were on the Moon or a planet which is **SMALLER** than Earth your weight would be **LESS** but your **MASS** would stay the same. Weight is calculated from **MASS** x **GRAVITATIONAL FIELD** strength. On Earth the **GRAVITATIONAL FIELD** strength is about **TEN** N/kg.

Q2 a) Arrow A is Thrust, Arrow B is Weight

b) i) FALSE
ii) FALSE
iii) FALSE
iv) TRUE
v) TRUE

Q3 <u>WEIGHT (N)</u>
234
37.5
12000
0.06

Q4

V	X	G	N	A	M	R	A	H	S
A	C	A	V	V	O	N	O	E	L
N	A	G	O	I	K	T	E	R	E
I	N	A	L	E	X	E	I	H	S
T	E	R	E	S	H	K	O	V	A
N	I	I	X	E	I	V	U	R	I
E	L	N	R	T	L	R	I	E	N
L	T	N	E	L	E	H	U	S	T
A	K	I	A	L	N	G	O	Y	R
V	G	N	O	R	T	S	M	R	A

Page 61

Q1 The astronauts have less weight because the Moon's gravity is weaker than Earth's.

Q2 a) The rocket is moving away from Earth and the force of gravity is weaker further away.

b) i) FALSE
ii) TRUE
iii) FALSE
iv) TRUE

c) i) 490.70N
ii) 0.55N
iii) 0.00N
iv) 85.65N

d) Its direction would be towards the centre of the Moon not the centre of the Earth.

Page 62

Q1 a) The earth is still
The Sun orbits round the Earth
The planets orbits round the Earth
Orbits are circles

b) GEOCENTRIC means that the Earth is at the centre.

c) Heliocentric

Q2 a) A GEOCENTRIC system:
Explains the daily motion of the Sun and Moon
Explains seasons
Can be used to predict eclipses

b) A HELIOCENTRIC system:-
Explains the daily motion of the Sun and Moon
Explains seasons
Fits in with the rules of gravity
Can be used to predict eclipses
Explains in a simple way why the planets seem to go backwards sometimes

Q3 Predicted a solar eclipse in 585BC: Thales of Miletus

Proposed an early heliocentric theory: Aristarchus of Samos

Published a book outlining the heliocentric theory: Nicolaus Copernicus

Provided very accurate observations: Tycho Brahe

Used ellipses for the planets' orbits which fitted perfectly with the observations: Johannes Kepler

Used a telescope and found Jupiter's moons and mountains on our Moon: Galileo Galilei

Produced a theory of gravity which explained why the planets move in ellipses: Isaac Newton

Page 63

Q1 a) D

b) A (or C, depending on where you're viewing the orbit from)

Q2 The **MOON** is the Earth's **NATURAL** satellite. It orbits once every **TWENTY SEVEN** days. It is kept in orbit due to Earth' **GRAVITATIONAL** force. The Moon feels a stronger force from the **EARTH** than from the Sun because it is much **CLOSER** to the **EARTH**.

Q3 a)

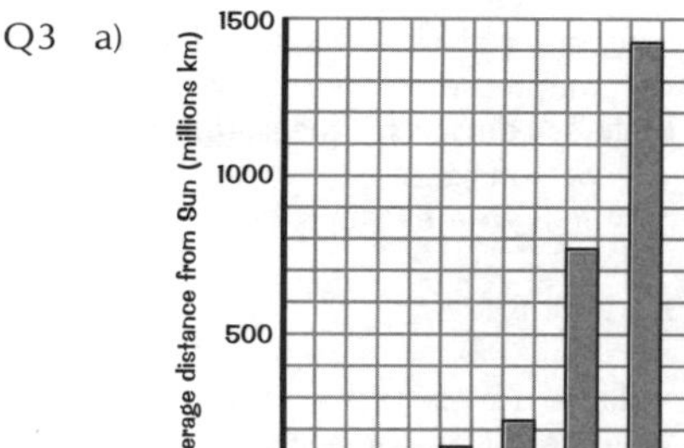

b) Average speed (**millions km per year**)
Mercury = 1517.67
Venus = 1093.94
Earth = 942.00
Mars = 761.62
Jupiter = 411.61
Saturn = 303.47

c) As you go further from the Sun the speed reduces.

d) The Sun's gravitational pull gets weaker the further out you go.

Page 64

Q1 a) FALSE
b) TRUE
c) TRUE
d) TRUE
e) FALSE
f) TRUE
g) FALSE
h) TRUE
i) FALSE

Q2 Some artificial satellites need to stay above a **FIXED** point on the Earth's surface. Satellites which do this include **COMMUNICATION** and **TV** satellites. This means that they must orbit the Earth **ONCE** every **24** hours. To make this happen they all have to be at the same **HEIGHT**. This type of orbit is called **GEOSTATIONARY**. The other main type of orbit is a **POLAR** orbit. This allows a satellite to scan **ALL** of the surface of the **EARTH**. **MILITARY** observation satellites use this sort of orbit.

Q3 a) Attraction
b) Centre
c) Newton
d) Weight
e) Mass
f) Thrust
g) Hubble
h) Mir
i) Galileo

Page 65

Q1 a) Distance (travelled)

b) i) Distance
ii) Time
iii) Stopwatch or stop clock

c) Acceleration

Q2 a) FALSE
b) TRUE
c) TRUE

The Answers

Q3 DISTANCE: cm, km, m, mm,
SPEED: m/s, km/h, cm/s, mm/s
TIME: s, h

Q4 SPEED = DISTANCE ÷ TIME

Q5 SPEED (m/s):
2
25
0.2

Q6 38.65 m/s (804 ÷ 20.8)

Q7 0.24 cm/s (33 ÷ 140)

Page 66

Q1 a) By reading the speedometer.
b) Distance travelled divided by time taken.
c) Her mother is talking about 'average speed', Roisin is talking about 'speed at a point'.

Q2 a) The times are very short, a person cannot react and operate the watch quickly enough so it would be inaccurate.
b) Increase
c) The car would accelerate more quickly.

Q3 a) TRUE c) FALSE
b) FALSE d) TRUE

Q4

DISTANCE	TIME	SPEED
5m	2s	2.5m/s
200km	4h	50km/h
1km	100s	10m/s

Page 67

Q1 a) Friction
b) Upthrust
c) Gravity
d) Thrust

Q2 a) X is thrust and Y is friction
b) X is gravity (or weight) and Y is friction (or air resistance)
c) X is gravity (or weight) and Y is upthrust
d) W is thrust, X is gravity (or weight), Y is upthrust and Z is friction (or water resistance)

Q3 a) Sprinters need to be STRONG to provide more FORCE for acceleration.
b) Sprinters need to be LIGHT as a small MASS will accelerate more quickly.
c) A HEAVY car will need more braking FORCE to stop it.
d) Racing cars are kept as light as possible to increase their ACCELERATION.

Q4 a) UNBALANCED
b) UNBALANCED
c) UNBALANCED
d) BALANCED
e) UNBALANCED

Page 68

Q1 a) When you walk or run you need a force to balance the frictional FORCE.
b) The frictional force you feel when you move through air is called air RESISTANCE.
c) When you move through WATER you will feel water resistance against you.
d) Dolphins have a STREAMLINED shape to reduce WATER resistance.
e) Streamlining is done to REDUCE the FRICTIONAL forces.

Q2 Sports where streamlining is very important could be cycling, swimming, motor racing, sprinting, skiing, sailing etc.

Q3 a) FALSE c) TRUE
b) TRUE d) FALSE

Q4 faster
still
resistance
particles
faster
more

Page 69

Q1 A, D, E

Q2 Diagram A ACCELERATING
Diagram B STEADY SPEED
Diagram C SLOWING DOWN
Diagram D STEADY SPEED

Q3 She jumps out of the plane
She accelerates
This is due to gravity pulling her down
This force stays the same
Air resistance pushes upwards on her
This force increases as she gets faster
Eventually the forces are balanced
She moves at a constant speed
She opens her parachute
This increases the air resistance
This slows her down
This reduces the air resistance
She moves at a slower constant speed
She lands

Q4 At A she is accelerating because her weight is greater than the air resistance
At B she is at a constant speed because the forces are balanced
At C she suddenly slows down because she opens her parachute
At D she is at a constant speed because the forces are balanced again

Page 70

Q1 a) pressure area
b) area pressure
c) area pressure
d) area pressure
e) area pressure

Q2 a) sharp teeth, small area, large pressure
b) snow shoes, large area, small pressure
c) stiletto heels, small area, large pressure. Elephant, large area feet, small pressure
d) large number of nails, fairly large area, fairly small pressure.

Q3 Blunt end, large area, small pressure, not able to stick in.

Q4 a) pressure = force ÷ area
b) pascal or N/m^2.
c) i) 5000 Pa
ii) 10 000 Pa
iii) 15 000 Pa
iv) 900 Pa

Page 71

Q1 The missing words are:
a) large
b) rapidly
c) more
d) closer together
e) increasing

Q2 a) gas under pressure
b) the gas escapes into the air, which is at lower pressure, taking liquid drops with it
c) danger of explosion of the punctured or heated can.

Q3 The missing words are:
a) heat
b) larger
c) increases
d) expands

Page 72

Q1 a) i) gets less
ii) an increased pressure or force
iii) no
iv) its pressure
v) got less
vi) pull the syringe out
b) i) stays the same
ii) increased pressure or force
iii) much closer
iv) water sprays out

Q2 a) i) 1000 Pa
ii) 1000 Pa, the same
iii) 5 cm

b)

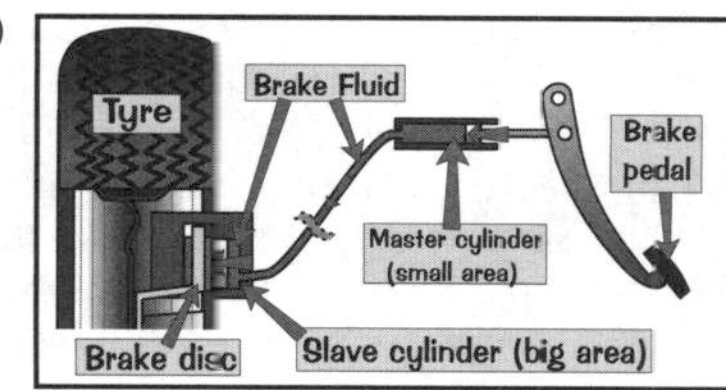

Pressure transmitted from master cylinder to slave cylinder through the brake fluid, which cannot be compressed.

Q3 a) water tank in loft
b) pressure caused by height of water above you
c) saline or blood held above patient
d) air pressure balanced by column of mercury about 0.76 m high.

The Answers

Page 73

Q1 In all the examples, the pivot is the point around which the turning takes place.
a) The force F acts on the outside of the example.
The force R acts on the thing being turned, much closer to the pivot.
b) Any 5 suitable examples, eg door handle, garlic crusher, egg slicer, etc.

Q2 a) i) pull
ii) pairs
iii) contracts
iv) contracts
v) elbow joint
b) other examples in the body of muscles working in pairs

Page 74

Q1 a) i) tips on Jane's side
ii) tips on Sophie's side
iii) tips on Sophie's side
iv) balances
b) 1 m from pivot

Q2 a) force times distance from pivot
b) 5 Nm
c) 500 Nm

Q3 a) i) 25 cm right
ii) 40 cm right
iii) 30 cm left
iv) 45 cm left
v) 30 cm right
vi) 40 cm right
vii) 20 cm left
viii) 50 cm right
b) sum of clockwise moments equals sum of anticlockwise moments.

Page 75

Q1 d), f)

Q2 a) do an experiment at school
b) use a book from the library
c) use the internet
d) contact the manufacturer
e) set up a model and collect data from it
f) do a survey outside

Q3 a) Bounce the balls on the same type of surface; drop them from the same height.
b) Do each type of exercise for the same length of time; make the same person do each exercise.
c) Use pieces of material which are the same size and thickness (if possible).

Q4 a) Does more sugar dissolve in hot water or in cold water?
b) Add sugar — 5g at a time — to 250cm^3 of cold water in a beaker. Stir. Keep on adding sugar until no more will dissolve. Repeat the whole experiment using hot water.
c) The masses of sugar added to the hot and cold water; the volume of water; the temperatures of each beaker of water.
d) Stir each beaker at the same speed and for the same length of time; use the same volumes of water.

Page 76

Q1 b)

Q2 a) burns, hot liquid in eye
b) burns
c) cuts, poisoning

Q3

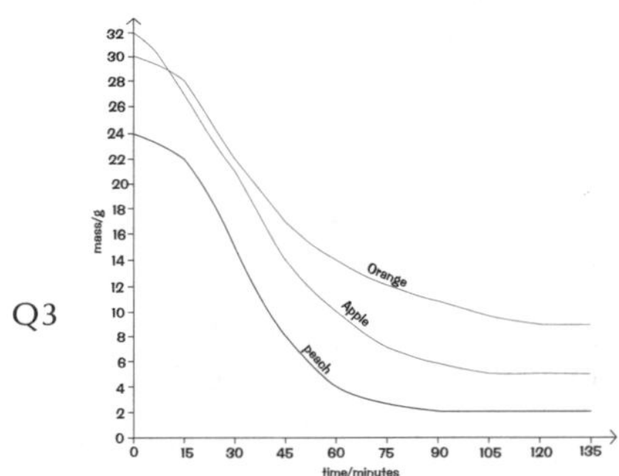

Q4 a) 70%
b) 92%

Q5 b)

Page 77

Q1 a) **Any 3 of the following:** use identical bottles/ make sure the starting temperature of the water is the same in both bottles/ use the same volume of water/ use the same thickness kitchen paper/ use the same thermometer/ make sure the temperature outside both bottles is the same.
b) (iii)
c) i) it can easily measure the temperature on the bottle's surface
ii) it is very accurate
iii) most schools have plenty of them

Q2 a) Wet Wendy
b) 11 minutes

Q3 **heat**, **evaporate**, **faster**, **urine**, **water**

Page 78

Q1 **variety**, **dry**, **fair**, **sunlight**, **pH**
Q2 **threw**, **identified**, **many times**, **dry**
Q3 a) whether she studied a wet or dry area
b) how many plant species were in each quadrat
Q4 a) grass, moss, buttercup, selfheal, sorrel, speedwell
b) 5
c) grass, moss, daisy
d) 2
e) 5.2
f) wet
Q5 Throw the quadrat more than 5 times in each area; repeat the experiment in another field.

Page 79

Q1 a) duckweed, water lettuce, water hyacinth, water soldier, Canadian pondweed, fanwort, spiked water milfoil, waterlily
b) bladder wrack, oarweed
Q2 a) duckweed, water lettuce, water hyacinth, water soldier
b) Canadian pondweed, fanwort, spiked water milfoil, waterlily
c) i) water soldier
ii) water lettuce & water hyacinth
Q3 a) duckweed, water lettuce, water hyacinth, water soldier, waterlily
b) They are all quite flat and broad
c) bladder wrack, oarweed, Canadian pondweed, fanwort, spiked water milfoil — they are all quite flexible and able to move with any currents in the water
Q4 a) fanwort and spiked water milfoil
b) bladder wrack and oarweed
c) Canadian pondweed
Q5 a) Could be in group N, as the leaves under the water are very fine and feathery; OR could be in group L as the leaves on the surface are floating, and are quite flat.
b) Group D, as the roots are anchored in the soil under the water.

Page 80

Q1 a) Rain is more acidic near big cities because cars produce lots of nitrogen oxide gases.
b) Rain is more acidic when the wind comes from the east because there are many coal-burning power stations in Europe to the east of the UK.
c) Rain is less acidic if it has been raining heavily for several days because the extra rain dilutes the acid.

Q2

Advantages of using secondary sources	Disadvantages of using secondary sources
It takes less time and effort to collect data	There may be no data for the place you're interested in
It doesn't matter if it doesn't rain when you want to get the information	You don't know if you can rely on the people who tested the pH
It's easy to get data for enough weeks to spot a trend	There may be no data for the weeks you're interested in

Q3 a) and b)

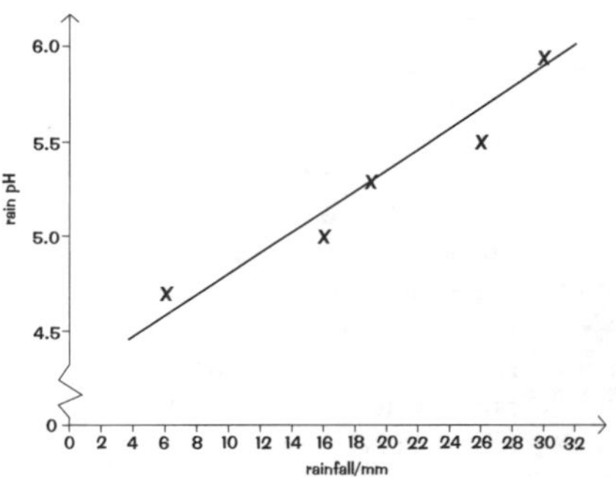

c) higher; less

Q4 Tom is still right, although the correlation between pH and rainfall is not as strong as his first graph showed.